PENGUIN BOOKS

BABY
WHISPERING

BABY
WHISPERING

Sharlene Poole

PENGUIN BOOKS

DISCLAIMER: My belief that settling or sleeping a baby on their side is safe when done so correctly is not supported by some health professionals. The World Health Organization and Plunket state that the safest way to sleep a baby is on their back. If you choose to use my method of settling always do so in conjunction with the advice of your doctor, midwife or lead maternity carer (LMC).

PENGUIN BOOKS
Published by the Penguin Group
Penguin Group (NZ), 67 Apollo Drive, Rosedale,
Auckland 0632, New Zealand (a division of Pearson New Zealand Ltd)
Penguin Group (USA) Inc., 375 Hudson Street,
New York, New York 10014, USA
Penguin Group (Canada), 90 Eglinton Avenue East, Suite 700, Toronto,
Ontario, M4P 2Y3, Canada (a division of Pearson Penguin Canada Inc.)
Penguin Books Ltd, 80 Strand, London, WC2R 0RL, England
Penguin Ireland, 25 St Stephen's Green,
Dublin 2, Ireland (a division of Penguin Books Ltd)
Penguin Group (Australia), 250 Camberwell Road, Camberwell,
Victoria 3124, Australia (a division of Pearson Australia Group Pty Ltd)
Penguin Books India Pvt Ltd, 11, Community Centre,
Panchsheel Park, New Delhi – 110 017, India
Penguin Books (South Africa) (Pty) Ltd, Block D, Rosebank Office Park,
181 Jan Smuts Avenue, Parktown North, Gauteng 2193, South Africa

Penguin Books Ltd, Registered Offices: 80 Strand, London, WC2R 0RL, England

First published by Penguin Group (NZ), 2012
3 5 7 9 10 8 6 4 2

Copyright © Sharlene Poole, 2012

The right of Sharlene Poole to be identified as the author of this work in terms of section 96 of the Copyright Act 1994 is hereby asserted.

Designed and typeset by Alice Bell
Illustrations by Deborah Hinde
Photographs on pages 10, 28, 88, 100, 112, 114, 128, 136 by iStockphoto.com;
page 7 by Greg Miller-Hard; page 21 Furness family collection
Printed in China through Asia Pacific Offset Ltd, Hong Kong

ISBN 978-0-143-56699-1

A catalogue record for this book is available
from the National Library of New Zealand.

www.penguin.co.nz

contents

acknowledgements

Firstly, I would like to thank all the babies around the world whom I have loved and learnt from and all the families who have entrusted me to guide them in caring for their babies. Without these families allowing me into their homes I would not have had the incredible opportunity to learn what I know today.

To my family, thank you. I have been surrounded by wonderful role models (my grandparents, my mother and father and aunties and uncles) since I was a child. Their love and good morals have formed the foundation of my approach to educating and supporting families and their babies.

Thank you to my friends and clients who have shown great confidence in what I do and who encouraged me through the journey of putting this book together.

I dedicate this book to my family: without your love I would not be where I am today.

introduction

The enormity of becoming a parent and the responsibility of caring for a baby can be overwhelming; hence my desire to provide a guide for new parents based on my years of experience and observation.

My understanding and knowledge-base comes from working as an early childhood teacher and from living with many families as a British maternity nurse. During this time it became apparent to me that while we are all different, personality-wise and in our beliefs and values, many of us have a common link: the desire to bring a baby up in this world to the best of our ability and to provide a loving and happy environment for the whole family.

When I started my business in New Zealand, which is based on providing guidance and advice to new parents, I soon learnt that all parents need support in some shape or form. We all seek advice, be it from family, friends, health professionals, books or the Internet, on how to be a good parent and how to cope with being a parent.

Often couples ask, 'Where is the manual?' when their baby is born, thinking to themselves, What do we do now that we are home? For some, it is a daunting role that lies ahead. While I do not like the word 'manual', I do understand why many parents in today's world ask this! We are a product of manuals and instruction at school and in the work place, and it seems only natural to wonder why, when suddenly we have the greatest and most challenging role ahead of us, there is no guide.

The concept of this book is to provide a parental guide, which offers parents and caregivers a simple and visual breakdown of the stages and changes in the first year of a baby's life. It is not designed to make you feel as if there is a right or wrong way of doing anything; rather, it is intended to highlight the issues that are common for families in the first year of a baby's life.

Becoming a parent is instinctive for some and less so for others; after all, we all come from different backgrounds. If, like me, you were surrounded by family and many baby cousins during childhood, motherly intuition can be ignited from an early age. Many parents I work with now, however, have never held a baby until their own is born.

I am convinced that we all have the ability to cope with being a parent, but personality, upbringing and current circumstances determine how easily we can tap into that intuition.

During the seven years I spent working as a maternity nurse in the UK, Europe, Japan, India, South Africa, Indonesia, Singapore, Russia and Australia, mostly for British ex-pat families, I gained incredible knowledge about how other cultures care for their babies and soon agreed with the saying, 'It takes a community to raise a child.' Each job and country expanded my knowledge-base and added to my understanding of a newborn's needs.

When you work 24 hours a day, six days a week for many years, you have the opportunity to see what works when trying to calm a baby and what doesn't, what some families like and others don't, while all the time gaining knowledge, asking questions and trialling methods, adapting them according to their success.

I, like so many other people, believe that babies are a product of their environment in most situations. Unless illness or health problems prevail, babies are born pure and wise, ready to be guided into the world we live in and to be nurtured through love and safe and calm surroundings.

At the beginning of my career I struggled to settle some babies. While I had training and a lot more knowledge than the new parents I was working for, I had no idea how to calm a baby who was unsettled for long periods of time and I didn't know of any other way of settling a baby to sleep other than rocking or using a dummy. It was the repetition of the job, and determination on my part, that encouraged me to create my own methods to replace or improve those that were 'the norm': for example, it did not sit well with me to leave a baby to cry for long periods of time each day or regularly.

Against the advice of some professionals I went back to settling a baby on the side, I went back to the belief that wind is a huge contributor to an unsettled newborn and I soon started to see great changes in the babies I was helping care for.

Since then I have continued to learn, adapt and problem-solve to gain a better understanding of the needs of individual families. I truly trust and believe in those techniques and recommendations that set me apart from other professionals in my industry – caring for and advising new parents.

CHAPTER 1

preparing for arrival

Where to begin? Preparing a loving, warm and safe environment for your baby are most important elements; everything else after this is a choice, a choice to spend time researching different methods and beliefs on raising children and a choice about how much money to spend setting up your home ready for the baby's arrival.

Children are born in different environments all around the world, each country having their own ways of doing things and their own ideas about what is needed when bringing a baby into this world. Working as a maternity nurse around the world, it has fascinated me to see these differences, especially the varying customs around daily practices, such as sleeping and feeding a baby, and simple things, like the products used.

Buying equipment can be a lot of fun, but much of what you may see or be advised to buy is actually not necessary. Sticking to the basics will provide you with enough to get started. It is better to spend where you find the need rather than over-stocking and never using some products; the rapid growth that a baby has in this first year is just unbelievable as is how many outfits or soft toys you end up never using!

When it comes to parenting styles you will be greatly influenced by family, friends, health professionals and written media. What you might observe and believe prior to becoming parents can change dramatically once you have your baby at home. It is important to keep an open mind about your options and ideas of what you will do once the baby has arrived. Still, having goals and plans is important and if you want to learn about raising a child, you can take full advantage of the many books and courses available in most communities. Just remember to remain open to change and new emotions.

TIPS TO PREPARE FOR YOUR NEW BABY

- Prepare meals for you and your partner and store in freezer.
- Wash baby's clothes (old or new) and have the essential 'first' items accessible ahead of time.
- Borrow or buy essential equipment (see list opposite).
- Think about the environment you are about to bring your baby home to: will it be adequately warm and dry? Is it a safe, loving and happy environment?
- Ask for support from your family or community.
- Prepare yourself physically – massage, yoga, Pilates and walking (always consult a doctor or health professional before undertaking exercise while pregnant).
- Don't organise too many things for the initial weeks, e.g. going away for a weekend or having people to stay. Every parent and every baby adapts to their new life in a different manner. Face each day as it comes with no expectations.
- Consider your birthing options/methods. There are a number of good books and regular courses focusing on birth. Your midwife or lead maternity carer (LMC) might recommend some books. Parents Centre and The Parenting Place run seminars for expectant parents and, of course, the Internet has a vast amount of information on these subjects.
- Plan for the set-up if birthing at home.
- Pack your bag for going to hospital.
- Hire or buy an infant car seat, or 'capsule' – you won't be able to leave the hospital without one!

Most people wish they had known so much more about the first weeks with their baby prior to the birth, but often your focus is only on the birth and a lot of information will just go over your head. So much goes out of your mind when you actually hold your baby in your arms.

One thing I suggest is that you try to be strong in communicating your feelings and concerns with those who influence you. Often I hear parents, particularly mothers, say that after the birth they felt bullied or pressured into making decisions they really did not believe in, or they felt their baby's needs were not met and they lacked the confidence to say what they truly wanted or felt to family, friends or professionals. Having a newborn can be overwhelming and you will be pretty exhausted so being confident can be hard, but you need to support each other as parents by communicating and asking questions when you do not understand.

Equipment list

Safety

* Baby car seat (capsule)

When purchasing or hiring a car seat be sure to have someone look at how it fits in your car. Not all car seats and capsules fit all cars. If the seat is not the right shape for your car it can tip too far forward, risking the baby's head and neck being incorrectly supported. Talk with a trained professional if you are uncertain.

* Baby thermometer

This is an item you must have in your house. If your baby seems very hot they may have a temperature which needs to be monitored. See your doctor promptly if you are concerned. There are two types of thermometer that I recommend: either one that takes the baby's temperature from their ear (which is very handy for quick access) or the simple style that you place underneath your baby's armpit.

Bedroom

* Moses basket/bassinet

Most new parents like to use a small bed (like a Moses basket or bassinet) to sleep their baby in, trying to replicate the small, cosy environment of the womb. However, it is not necessary to have either as long as where you are sleeping your baby is warm, dry and safe.

The brilliant thing about a Moses basket or bassinet is that you can move them around, sleeping your baby near you during the day, say in the lounge for the initial weeks, or by your bed at night.

Buying a new mattress or using a clean, well-cared-for mattress is vital; however, the basket or bassinet itself can be pre-loved or borrowed as your baby is in it for such a short period of time – some as little as six weeks and some as long as six months.

* Cot
This is not important to have from day one unless you decide to sleep your baby in a bassinet that attaches inside the cot, or you choose to sleep your baby in one from the beginning. Don't be tempted to buy frilly or fancy cot duvet and bumper sets; these are not always safe.

* Changing table
This can make changing a baby an easier process. Using a towel or waterproof mat on the floor is equally as good for those who find that comfortable, but I must stress that you make sure you are not bending over a low bed or table as the repetition can cause lower back problems, especially for mothers post-birth or those with previous back injuries.

* Baby monitor
I only recommend these when you have a large house and you are sleeping a baby in a room quite some distance away from you, especially in the daytime. In my experience, couples who use monitors every moment can become hypersensitive and jumpy or feel alarmed when a baby makes noises in their sleep.

* Low-wattage light bulb
This is very handy when you are feeding in the night, especially if you have a visual and inquisitive baby! Turning on a bright light can wake some babies up too much and make them harder to settle.

* Room thermometer
This is great to have until you get to know the ideal room temperature for your baby. Some baby monitors have them built-in, but I have always found that they are a little out in their readings. You are always best, if concerned about your baby's body temperature, to check by placing your hand under their clothes, between their shoulder blades.

* Thermostatic heater
A lot of houses in New Zealand need some kind of heating in winter or cooler months in the year. I like to use a heater that has a thermostat or timer in a baby's bedroom so that it does not overheat. If you have a heat pump or central heating in your home, ensure that you air the room daily when possible.

Bedding

* 2–4 x Moses basket/bassinet-size cotton fitted sheets

* 2 x Moses basket/bassinet-size cotton flat sheets

* 1 x 100% cotton blanket

* 1 x woollen blanket

* 6 x cotton wraps (swaddles) about 1-metre square

You can start with smaller sized wraps, but to save on buying more you can just fold a large square into a triangle to suit a smaller baby and use cloth nappies when they are first born.

* Wedge or rolled hand towel

This is something I recommend if you are using my 'in and out of the room' settling technique as it helps to keep your baby on their side while you settle them. (See Side Settling on page 72 for information on its use.) Baby First is the brand I recommend for this purpose.

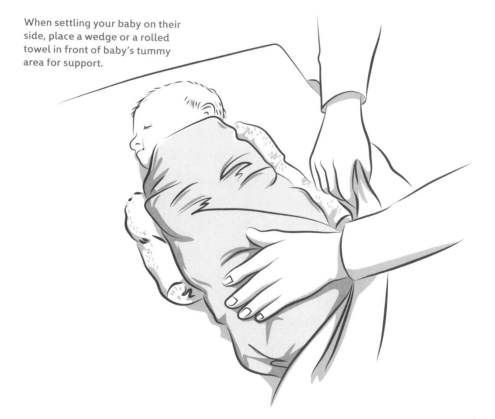

When settling your baby on their side, place a wedge or a rolled towel in front of baby's tummy area for support.

* Mattress protector

I am an advocate of natural mattress protectors that do not use a plastic or synthetic waterproof fabric, as they allow the baby to keep an even body temperature when lying in bed, particularly in the summer months. You can choose a 'Dry Cot', a New Zealand woollen mattress protector or one of the many cotton protectors available from your leading baby stores.

BEDROOM SET-UP TIPS

- I suggest you position your baby's bed away from any window if you can to avoid draughts, especially in winter.

- If you have blinds or curtains that have drawstrings, make sure the cot is placed well away from them. If it is too close to the drawstrings an older baby may be able to reach them.

- Limit the use of bright or stimulating toys or pictures in the room until you know your baby's personality. Some babies are 'visual' and can be a little overwhelmed or find it hard to settle to sleep if there is too much to look at.

- I like to use a flat cotton cloth nappy under the baby's head area of the bassinet to help soak up and catch any spills that might occur and it reduces the amount of bed changing you have to do!

Keeping active

* Buggy or pram

Now this is the fun but sometimes expensive part! There are so many styles to choose from today. From my experience using a huge variety, I would suggest you go for a buggy or pram that has the ability to have a newborn lying flat, is easy to put up and down and to fit in your car or home. My favourite is a 3-wheel buggy, not just because they move across various terrains with ease, but also because they encourage you to walk a little quicker than others and that is good for exercise.

Insect net for pram

When you live in or travel to tropical countries, like Singapore, using an insect net is a good idea. These can be fitted over a buggy and some even fit over a baby's bed. While mosquitoes are not as harmful in New Zealand as they are in some countries, they can irritate some babies.

Sling or front pack

Again, not a vital purchase, but if you like to walk where there are steps, you want to take your baby to the supermarket or you intend to travel, then it will be useful. Be conscious of the positioning of some slings; there are many styles for sale today, but not all distribute the weight of the baby evenly for your back.

* Sheepskin

This classic New Zealand product is often overlooked today! I love sheepskins because you can use them in many ways, especially under a mat while your baby is having floor play.

Basic clothing

* 4 x newborn short-sleeve singlets (onesies) that do up between legs

I prefer the button between the leg singlets as they don't ride up when you are winding or handling the baby. Also they keep the baby's lower back warm during the cooler months.

* 2 x woollen singlets (if born in spring/autumn and winter)

Merino, wool or wool/cotton mixes are all available today, from the cheaper brands to more expensive. If you discover your baby has sensitive skin, place a cotton singlet on first to prevent any irritation.

* 3 x day outfits

All-in-one, jumpsuit-style outfits that do up in the front are best. Those with buttons or a zip down the back can be uncomfortable when winding or sleeping baby on their back. I prefer to use all-in-one outfits rather than a two-piece as they are more comfortable around a baby's tummy.

* 2 x nighties

These old-fashioned but practically designed outfits are great for nappy changing at night and very comfortable for the baby. Place a pair of socks or booties, or even little woollen leggings in cold climates, underneath.

* 1 x cotton cardigan and 1 x woollen cardigan

The season and climate you are living in will dictate whether you need to have both a woollen and cotton cardigan. Most newborn babies need a woollen cardigan throughout the year in New Zealand as temperatures at night can drop all year round.

* 2 x cotton socks or booties

They are a pain to keep on but are a necessary item if your baby is not wearing an outfit that has built-in feet! You can get cotton or woollen booties that are not only warm but also tie onto the foot to keep them on a little better. In cold months, I place a pair of socks underneath an outfit with built-in feet.

* 1 x cotton hat and 1 x woollen hat

A newborn baby should always have a hat on when out and about and, in some cases when they are first born, even inside if it is quite a cold house.

* 1 x baby shawl/blanket

This is for leaving the hospital or when you are out and about. It can be the same blanket that is used in your baby's bed; choose one that is light and not too bulky. Fleece blankets are great for outings, but I prefer to use natural fibres when they are sleeping in their bed.

Feeding (breast and bottle)

* Feeding pillow

This is an optional extra really as you can easily use a pillow from the bedroom to help support your baby while you are breastfeeding or giving them a bottle. Most mums find using a pillow is vital when they are learning to breastfeed as it helps to support the baby's weight. Your neck, shoulders and arms have a little adjusting to do and get quite tired when feeding regularly in the early weeks.

* Clock

I find that having a clock that you can see in the dark is handy for when you are feeding at night. Some have built-in night-lights as well, which can be useful!

* Breast pads

There are washable or natural biodegradable breast pads on the market today, alongside the standard throw-away brands you can get from supermarkets and baby stores. I hear good feedback about the washable wool or bamboo pads available.

* Nipple cream

There are many nipple creams on the market. One thing to note if you are using nipple cream is that it should only be used little and often. Most creams are okay to leave on the nipple before a feed, not requiring you to clean off the nipple, but check before use. If you find your baby is struggling to latch to the breast, try wiping the cream off, especially around the areola area as the taste or slipperiness may be making it hard for your baby. For product suggestions talk with your midwife or health professional.

* Nipple shields

This product is designed to help with breastfeeding if mothers are suffering from cracked nipples. It is a silicone shield that sits over the nipple and areola area. Women with flat or inverted nipples may also find these helpful in the initial weeks when learning to feed baby.

* Breast pump

A lot of women will not need a breast pump but for those mothers who require assistance to maintain a good milk supply or who might be returning to work, my suggestion would be to purchase one that offers a good enough suction for your individual supply. Mothers with an abundance of milk might be fine to use a hand pump while others may need to hire or purchase a double breast pump that is more efficient. Talk with your midwife or health professional if you are unsure. The Medela range is the one that I recommend mostly.

* Bottles and breastfeeding

Even if you are determined to breastfeed your baby I would advise that you have a bottle on standby, as you never know how things are going to go. In my experience, if you suddenly find you need to use a bottle you won't want to have to rush out and buy one; you will want to be as organised as possible. Some mothers will want to use a bottle as a back-up to their breastfeeding. If you choose to do this, I recommend that you establish your breastfeeding before using a bottle regularly.

2 x 100 ml (BPA-free or glass) bottles

Look for bottles that help to encourage a baby to suck as they would on the breast. See www.sharlenepoole.com for recommendations. These are good to use when you are mainly breastfeeding but may need a bottle on occasion.

2 x newborn teats

Most bottles come with teats for a newborn baby but sometimes the teat is a little fast and can create more wind for them. There is a teat called a 'Chu Chu' which acts similarly to the Medela 'Calma' teat and helps a baby suck a little more like on the breast. They are designed to fit most narrow neck bottles. For information on where to purchase these teats I would suggest you Google 'Chu Chu teat', as they are not widely available in baby shops.

* Exclusively bottle feeding

Some mothers will choose not to breastfeed or may be unable to for health reasons. They will need to have a little more equipment than mentioned above. I suggest the following when bottle feeding:

6–8 x 100 ml bottles

The bottles that I like to use most of all are BPA-free or glass. See www.sharlenepoole.com for recommendations.

6 x 180–200 ml bottles

I prefer not to use big bottles with newborn babies, or small babies that are not having large volumes of milk, as big bottles tend to give them more wind.

* Infant formula

Talk with a health professional about the products they recommend and for advice. There are a lot of products to choose from and it can be a little overwhelming. There are also formulas designed for babies with food intolerances or allergies. Your doctor or health professional will be able to provide you with more information.

* Bottle and teat brushes

It is important to scrub the bottles out after use, even when using a dishwasher, as both expressed breast milk and infant formula are very fatty and can leave a film on the inside of the bottle if not cleaned thoroughly before sterilising. Some bottle brushes also come with teat brushes.

Placing a little salt in the end of the teat, rubbing the teat between your fingers and then thoroughly rinsing will remove the fatty film well.

* Steriliser

You do not have to spend a lot of money here, it really comes down to practicality and safety. If you are only occasionally using a bottle then sterilising the 'old-fashioned way' is fine for most; that is, boiling your bottle and teat in water for three minutes. (See page 48 for more information on sterilising.) This can be unsafe when you are tired – I suggest you use a timer so you do not forget!

A microwave, or steam-unit steriliser is what most parents use today to sterilise the bottles without the use of chemicals. The brand I like best for this is Avent; it is compact and easy to use.

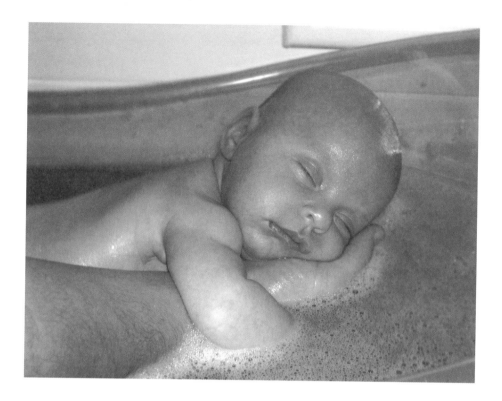

Bathing and changing

* Baby bath

This is not always necessary; babies can bathe in a clean sink if it's big enough or in the big bath or shower with you. But baby baths are handy to have as you can bathe your baby at a height that is suitable for you. On a clean kitchen bench is often a good place, or you can get a bath stand, or bath and changing table in one.

* Natural bath products

Your newborn baby won't get very dirty and I try to limit the use of too many products in their baths while they are small, but once or twice a week the use of a natural bath wash and shampoo is a good idea. I prefer to use natural products as they are gentle on a baby's delicate skin.

* Wash bowl

This is for 'top and tail' washes (days when your baby doesn't have a bath you can give them a little wash, top and bottom!) or if you are choosing to use washable wipes and water for nappy changing. Just make sure you use a different bowl or it is cleaned well if using for both wiping a dirty bottom and washing a face. A small kitchen bowl is fine, I find a stainless steel bowl is good as it is safe and keeps water warmer for longer.

* Thermos
Enables you to have warm water on hand for cleaning baby's face and bottom.

* Small cotton face cloths
You can just use your normal face cloths or flannels but I find that for newborns the soft and gentle ones designed for babies are best.

* Bamboo or washable cloth nappy liners
I like to use biodegradable bamboo or soft, washable cloth nappy liners on a daily basis for babies, particularly when they are newborn and often have a dirty nappy every time they feed! The bamboo nappy liners are soft and fantastic as they can be flushed down the toilet or they biodegrade in your rubbish. If using washable cloths, buy coloured ones so you can identify them from face cloths.

* Baby wipes (unscented)
There are times when having baby wipes are handy, like when travelling in the car. Each baby's skin is different and I would suggest that you watch your baby's bottom when using wipes as some babies can be sensitive to the product they use to keep them moist, even natural ingredients. When a baby has nappy rash, stop using wipes and just use water until it has healed.

* Natural nappy changing cream or antiseptic zinc-based cream
It is always good to have both a natural cream and an antiseptic zinc-based cream (such as Sudocrem) on hand in case needed. If the baby's bottom is always patted dry after they have been changed before using the cream, it helps the skin to absorb the cream. I use a natural cream daily and after changing a dirty nappy. Most of the time you will not need to use a lot of antiseptic zinc-based cream on a baby's bottom, but keep it for when the bottom is looking a little pink or sore.

* 2 x newborn pack of disposable nappies
I like to support our environment by suggesting parents choose to use washable or biodegradable nappies, such as Moltex. While disposables are a wonderful invention, and the only option for some, both the environmental impact and chemical use in the standard disposables is something I prefer not to recommend.

One thing to note when your baby is getting bigger is to not buy nappies by the size on the packet but by how well they fit your baby. When the sides of the nappy do not overlap or there are red marks around your baby's inner thigh, it is time to change up a size. Nappies are better to be slightly too big than too small.

* 6–12 x cotton cloth square nappies

The famous New Zealand cloth nappies are brilliant for everything! They are great as nappies, a spill cloth, under a baby's head in bed to reduce sheet washing or as a changing mat. Any cotton cloth is fine, though the thicker the weave of fabric the better.

* Bucket with lid

This is a recommendation from the past when cloth nappies were soaked in a big bucket (with a lid for its safe use). Even though you might not be using cloth nappies, a bucket with a lid is very handy as baby's clothes, bibs, sheets, etc. often need to be soaked.

* Baby washing powder or liquid

Like any product I use for a baby, the more natural the washing powder is, the better, both for the environment and a baby's skin. There are washing products available with little or no fragrance that are particularly good for babies with sensitive skin.

* Olive oil or sweet almond oil

Most babies when first born 'shed' a layer of skin and most treated water is a little drying on their skin. Placing a drop or two of oil in the bath or massaging your baby after a bath with a few drops of oil will help to put moisture back into their skin.

* Baby nail scissors/clippers

I prefer to use nail scissors as you are able to see what you are doing a little more easily, but you can buy packs that have both.

* Baby brush

To help the prevention of cradle cap I suggest you brush your baby's hair after you have dried it. This helps to stimulate the scalp.

* Natural drops

When I was a novice working with newborn babies 24 hours a day, I relied on using natural remedies or, occasionally, Infacol or Gripe Water to assist with a baby's wind. Having the correct diet for a breastfeeding mother or the right teat on a bottle, along with effective winding should mean few additional products are needed, but it is good to have something on hand while you are learning and if your baby suffers from excess wind or digestion trouble.

Working together as a couple and as parents

Bringing a baby into a relationship is for many a wonderful addition and can strengthen the love you have for one another. The incredible miracles that babies are and the joy that they bring give a whole new dimension to the word 'love'.

Having had the honour of living with and working alongside many first-time (and many many-time-over!) parents, I have witnessed, guided and counselled couples who find their new baby's needs and their responsibility as a parent a challenge for their relationship.

Mothers of newborns are tired, hormonal and often emotional. This can affect their ability to think logically and when their partners try to help, often their reaction is not what their partner wants to hear!

Fathers will never quite understand what a mother is going through and therefore, at times, some advice or deliverance of advice can appear a little black-and-white and can be difficult for a mother to cope with.

Frequently, when a mother is struggling to settle their baby, a father will come into the room with a 'fresh' pair of eyes and will be able to settle the baby in seconds. Even though, logically, the mother is happy that the baby has been calmed, it can be very deflating for her as she may feel she should be able to do it every time. I encourage both partners to deal with such situations as follows:

- Be patient with each other. Mothers are tired and fragile and need extra care, especially in trying situations. Fathers/partners deserve to be listened to; they have also been working all day and are tired. They can often look at situations from another perspective and their view, advice or calm presence can be just what you all need.
- Communicate with each other. Think carefully about how you deliver advice/help and how you respond to one another.

Babies are very intuitive, their senses are incredibly heightened and they will possibly be unsettled if both parents are unhappy. They are little sponges: they learn, grow and feel secure when their environment is calm and safe.

TIPS ON HOW TO MANAGE OR ASK FOR HELP

- Ask for help in a manner that suits you. Suggest the best time of day for you.
- Organise 'Granny' or 'Poppa' days. This can be a regular Skype call for those away from home or a visit or outing together – even a day's help in the house.
- Share your methods of parenting with your parents or in-laws so they can understand and can see how to help.
- Listen to and observe the way a grandparent or older role model interacts with your baby. Often they will remember skills and games that you were taught as a child.

- Respect each other's perspectives. If you disagree or cannot work together, seek advice from a mutual party.
- Be aware of your baby. Babies are very intuitive, their senses are incredibly heightened and they will possibly be unsettled if both parents are unhappy. They are little sponges: they learn, grow and feel secure when their environment is calm and safe.

The role of a grandparent or supportive figure

A mature, experienced role model or supportive figure during your early months and years of parenting is an unbelievable gift and resource. The role of a grandparent, for example, is something we often forget to give credit to.

Whether you have a parent, aunt or a neighbour, encouraging their involvement in your life can bring many valuable skills to your journey as a parent.

In every country I have been to outside the Western world, I have seen the vital role grandparents play in bringing up a newborn baby through to their early childhood years. Today, in New Zealand, I also see families who are well supported by grandparents, but more often than not one or both parents live away from their hometown or country. We are also living in a time when a lot of grandparents are still working and are unable to be as much help as they would like to be.

'Grandparenthood' is such a natural progression from being a parent. As I have seen throughout my career and am now observing in my own mother as she embarks on being a grandmother, the desire to be a part of your and your baby's life is huge and has a very strong pull on the heart.

Compared to the past, many couples having babies today have a lot more independence and are exposed to a lot more advice than their parents were. This can lead them to believe they are the 'experts' and their parents or in-laws the 'novices'! While a lot of information or advice has been adapted or changed, your parents did manage to bring you up and, depending on the circumstances, brought you up well. Be mindful that they have been there before and do understand a lot more than you probably realise and their desire to help you is part of the cycle of life.

There are, of course, times when the advice from these 'older' figures can contradict current practices or your beliefs. Whether it is a custom of the family, a cultural belief or their experience of having had children themselves, it is your choice as a parent whether you follow their advice. You must choose what is right for you and your baby. If it is concerned with the health of the baby, however, it is always best to follow the advice of a health professional.

I often suggest to clients who do not have a relative nearby to see if a neighbour or the mother or mother-in-law of a close friend would meet with them occasionally. Often all we have to do is ask as many people who have the time would love to watch a sleeping baby while you rest or do a kindy pick-up, or do some cooking for you.

Apart from their help and support we can learn a lot from our parents and in-laws. The wise, calming words that many of the older generation have regarding children can be inspiring; they are often more patient and have memories to share that let you know they understand.

While much advice on a baby's health and well-being has changed since your parents raised you, it is still wise to listen. There is a lot of information that is still very helpful and valid but we have to give grandparents the opportunity to share and suggest. I often hear clients say 'Oh! That is what my mum said', after I have given my suggestions!

Your labour bag
* For you:
2 night shirts or pyjamas (button front for feeding)
2 nursing bras
Comfortable underwear
Maternity pads
Water bottle
Snacks
Magazine/book
Notebook and antenatal documents
Music and headphones
Aromatherapy oil or birthing remedies (talk with
    your midwife or naturopath)
Toiletries
Camera
Comfortable clothes for you to wear home

* For baby:
2 singlets/vests (1 cotton and 1 wool)
2 outfits
Socks or booties
Hat
Swaddle or wrap
Baby blanket (light wool)
Nappies
Bamboo nappy liners to use as wipes with water
Natural nappy cream
Dummy

Remember to have the baby's car seat in the car before you
leave for the hospital as some hospitals require you to transfer
to other facilities within hours of your baby being born.

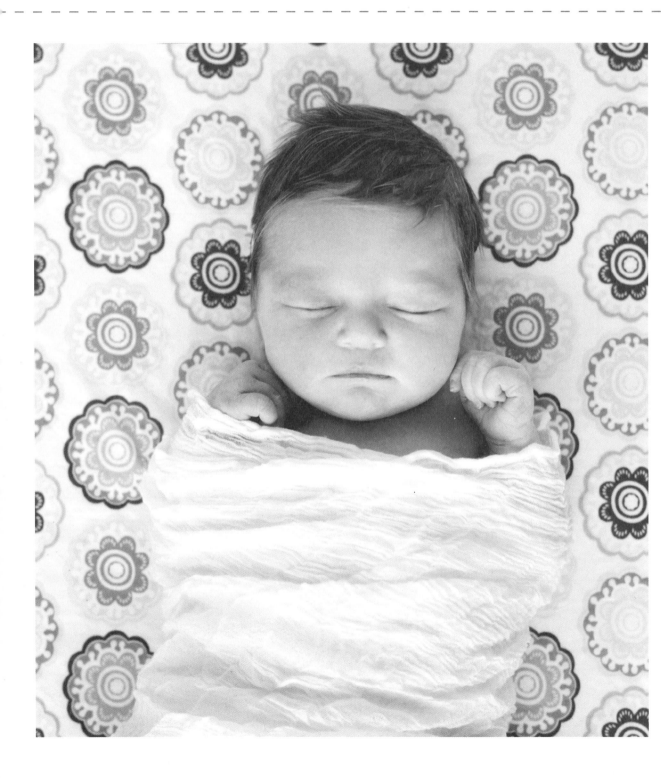

CHAPTER 2

newborn: 0–3 weeks

I like to call these first three weeks of a baby's life the 'honeymoon period' as Nature has in most cases given you a sleepy, content baby to bond with and time for you to establish some confidence.

Basic needs: 0–3 weeks

- Bond with your baby and take time to learn about each other – learn to love each other.
- Limit their awake time – most new babies only cope with 40–60 minutes.
- Limit stimulation.
- Feed frequently – on demand or roughly 2–3 hourly.
- Have patience when they are feeding and when bringing up their wind.
- Winding is vital for most babies once your milk has 'come in'.
- Rest is important for your milk supply and for the long hours of caring for a newborn baby. (Dads and partners need rest, too!)
- Eat well – make sure you eat healthy foods that are suitable for your baby's digestion.
- Ignore conflicting advice – find a few family members, friends or professionals whom you respect and trust to support you.
- Learn effective settling techniques to help you in the future – this is the foundation time for you and your baby.
- Be open to creating a daily pattern for you to manage all the tasks a new parent has. A strict routine is too rigid for most babies in the first three weeks but you can start creating little patterns for your household if this makes you feel more settled (see page 144).
- Learn the majority/minority rule – Focus on how things are going for the majority of the time, not the minority! Remember the many times you have successfully fed, winded, settled or bathed your baby during the week, not the few times you may have struggled.

Everything is new for you and the learning process has begun. Cleverly, however, you have plenty of time to practise attending to your baby's needs as the repetition of feeding, sleeping and changing is constant.

Everyone is vulnerable at this time: mums are often on an emotional rollercoaster and dads or partners have a great desire to be able to problem-solve and seek answers to all the 'unknown' questions, while providing support for their partner.

In my opinion, what your baby needs from you in these first three weeks is love through touch, warmth and patience, and food. This is the time to focus on bonding with your baby through skin-to-skin contact and learning about each other. Limit visitors so you can become confident with feeding, both breast and/or bottle, and learning to settle your baby. This can be difficult as everyone will want to meet your baby, but they will understand.

The old saying 'all a newborn baby does is cry, feed and have dirty nappies' is not quite right in my opinion. If you are meeting their needs by understanding the cues they give you, there are very limited tears. These incredible newborn babies are so vulnerable, yet so smart at communicating their important needs: they cry to say I am hungry and tired, or I have a sore tummy, and stop when their need is met.

Some parents will not fully experience this 'honeymoon period' because they have a premature baby, who might need assistance in the hospital for these initial weeks, or they have a baby who is born, as I call it, a 'wise owl'. The wise owl is alert from day one and is not too happy about waiting for a mother's milk to come in or for that confidence to calm them!

While I have no fixed opinion on how a newborn baby is brought up, I do believe there is a method of parenting that helps a new parent cope with bringing up a baby alone or with little support: a consistent approach and a tried and tested routine.

Babies are incredibly intelligent and receptive to their environment and if you as their mother are happy, so too will your baby be, however you choose to parent.

Happy Mother, Happy Baby!

> *What your baby needs from you in these first three weeks is love through touch, warmth and patience, and food. This is the time to focus on bonding with your baby through skin-to-skin contact and learning about each other.*

Food for thought
Choosing a parenting style

You are about to be exposed to a lot of different opinions when it comes to caring for a baby or child. Some have the confidence to choose their own journey as parents and have the ability to 'filter' the information given to them, while others try to do as they have been told or want to have the best baby and so try everything to achieve this.

What you, as parents, must do is be aware – be aware of your baby's needs first, be aware of your own feelings and choices, and be aware of those who want to help but may be stepping over the line by only sharing knowledge from their experience rather than from well-practised or researched information.

Cuddling to sleep

It is very important to bond with your baby through cuddling or snuggling; they relax and feel warm and safe when being held in your arms. Just as important though is time for you, looking after your needs as a new mum or dad and you both as a couple.

Babies are very wise and learn quickly that they like to be held until they fall asleep rather than being put down to sleep in a bed. There is no problem with this approach but be aware that creating a habit like this can last for some time.

Most parents whom I advise tell me they would like their baby to sleep in a bed so they can have time for other siblings or business. Knowing this and knowing how babies learn from the beginning what is a daily normality, I suggest that you 'start as you mean to go on'.

Start by having cuddles after a feed and putting your baby down to bed awake but sleepy for the most part. Then allow your baby to fall asleep with you some of the time. Working out what times in the day you have for these special snuggles and when you would like your baby to be sleeping in bed helps to get into a routine that suits you and in turn your baby. Babies love to be guided and thrive on routine and stability. (For more on routines see page 145.)

Noise

When babies are first born they can sleep through most noise in the house or environment. Most can sleep through vacuuming, washing machines and talking.

However, when I started working with newborns and their families I found that sometimes they just needed some quieter moments to get off to sleep, for example, when they are a little over-tired and stimulated after being out or having visitors. By removing them to a quieter space they would calm quickly and settle into a deep sleep, then be able to cope and be surrounded by sound again.

If this is your first baby, I suggest having consistent sound around during the day so they don't get too used to absolute silence. Try having background noise, like a radio or music playing – this way they will not be woken as easily down the track by sudden sounds such as a phone ringing, a door shutting or guests arriving.

Of course, if this is your second or third baby then there will always be consistent noise around! Using a 'white noise' CD in your baby's room might help them to cope with sibling noise.

Premature babies

Alongside the possible shock of having your baby earlier than you expected, you might have to deal with being separated from them in hospital and not getting to go home as quickly as you thought you would. This can be challenging. The knowledge that your baby is being cared for is comforting and I suggest you take advantage of the people around you and your baby, who are trained to support and educate you to the best of their knowledge.

If your baby is spending time in hospital they will still know you are near and that you love them, even if it is just from the touch of your finger or the sound of your voice.

Once your baby is able to come home, enjoy plenty of skin-to-skin contact to help you bond in your own environment – this will be your first and most important task. Don't think about the future too much, just take one day at a time.

I often get asked by mums with premature babies how far 'behind' their baby is developmentally and emotionally compared to those born full term. That is a hard question to answer as all babies are different and I suggest that it is best to talk with a doctor about this. From there you can work out how best to care for your baby and what can be expected of them individually.

Please note: Some of my techniques or suggestions, like side settling, are not appropriate for premature babies until they have reached the stage where you no longer would classify them as being a premature baby – once they are strong and healthy.

Multiples

One baby is a lot for new parents to manage let alone twins or triplets! It is a blessing, in my opinion, when you have multiples but it might not feel like it at the time, particularly for the first 3–6 months (for some this can be up to one year) of their lives.

From my experience as a godmother to twins and having worked with many families with multiples, what is most important after the babies' health and well-being is the support you have.

You do need to be incredibly well organised to 'manage' the loads of washing, long feeding and winding times and settling your babies. Being organised with meals in the freezer or by saying 'yes' to the many family, friends or neighbours who offer help will make the initial weeks more manageable. This is no time to be a martyr, it is time to accept help and perhaps be more organised than you would normally be!

When I was helping one particular family with their triplets I was amazed at the amount of support they had as well as how well the mother was coping with so many people in their home. This can be a very emotional time and when you cannot just be a 'mum' alone it can be challenging.

I advise all parents that if they are struggling to settle their baby to make sure they do not over-stimulate them, especially in their first six weeks of life. This can be very hard when you have people in your house to help, so what I suggest is that you create a roster or schedule. It sounds so military-like, I know, but having everything written down, who is here to help at this time, who is dropping off a meal and so on, will minimise the time you spend thinking about day-to-day requirements and allow you more time to concentrate on being a mother or father for your babies. What I remind families is that their babies are individuals with their own personalities and what works for one baby might not work for the other(s).

The triplets' mum wrote down the basic steps for settling and stuck them to the wall of the babies' room to help keep things consistent for the babies. Everyone has their different ways of doing things but when you have more than one baby it is handy to have some kind of consistency. When you are using a settling technique like mine (see page 73), you may have to consider using a dummy in conjunction with the hands-on approach. It can be upsetting if one baby is crying while you are in the middle of 'topping up' or changing the other.

I do suggest to all parents with multiples, unless they have 24-hour-a-day help, that they put their babies on routine instead of demand feeding. I have seen too many mothers struggle with lack of sleep when feeding two or more babies on demand. Even though each baby is different, it is the only way most parents will be able to cope with double or triple the work.

Common questions: 0–3 weeks

Why doesn't my baby have many wet or dirty nappies?

You need to talk to your health professional straight away if there have been no wet nappies in 24 hours. A well hydrated baby should be having several wet nappies in a day – if not at every feed time, then at least every other feed.

It is quite common for some babies not to have a dirty nappy for several days, while others can dirty their nappy at every feed. In my opinion, if your baby doesn't have a dirty nappy and is unhappy it may be that something you have eaten has had an effect on them. While some babies are settled and only have a bowel motion every other day, those who have bowel motions every 3–5 days are possibly unsettled and not feeding and sleeping as well as they could be. Dairy is a food that I commonly see affecting babies. In any case, if you are concerned or your baby is not happy, always seek advice from your doctor and/or naturopath.

Why do I feel so overwhelmed?

This is a very emotional time for new parents. Both mothers and fathers can find the incredible gift of being a parent completely overwhelming.

If you have experienced a challenging birth you may need time to bond with your baby and recover physically.

Being sleep deprived is one of the hardest things to deal with in the early weeks. When we are tired we are often not able to cope as well, so getting plenty of rest is essential. Keep things simple. Don't listen to every piece of advice: too many opinions from those around you can confuse you when you are tired.

If you feel at all like you are not able to cope or if you are concerned about how your partner is coping, seek advice from a health professional like your midwife, nurse or doctor. Postnatal distress is a very common condition and it should not be taken lightly (see page 165 for an organisation offering support and advice).

How do I gain confidence as a parent?

It takes time for every parent to gain confidence and you need to give yourself and your baby time to learn and grow together. Surround yourself with people and an environment that encourages this. Choosing to attend one of the many courses available in your community or seeking advice in your home might be an option, if you feel you need help.

How can I help my children adjust to our new baby?

It is important that you involve older children when a new baby arrives. Let them gently touch and get to know the baby; children are full of discovery and as long as you are there to guide them it should be encouraged. Bathing, rocking or holding the baby with your help are enjoyable activities for them to be involved in.

If you find that older children are tricky to manage and you are experiencing behaviour that you have not seen before, remember that this is a challenging time for them. They might not be spending as much time with you as before and they will often seek attention through behaviour they know you do not like.

Try to distract or involve them instead of always saying 'No'. For example, you could create a 'special box' with activities for times when you are focusing on your new baby – it is both a reward and a distraction for older siblings.

How do I deal with conflicting advice on how to care for my baby?

You may have family and friends who offer you help or suggest a certain way of caring for your baby. Alongside this you will have your health professional helping and guiding you. If you find it all confusing or that the advice is conflicting you need to take time out, alone or with your partner, and discuss what you both believe in and what advice you would like to follow. There is no right or wrong way of doing things once you have met the basic health and safety needs of a baby (feeding them well so they are gaining weight, keeping them warm and loving them by providing a safe environment).

Everyone has an opinion when it comes to the care of babies. Watch and learn from like-minded people whose recommendations you feel comfortable with. Talk with a professional you trust and respect and see if they can help you find what works for you and your family.

When is it okay to start a routine?

If you know what you are doing or have assistance in doing so, then I believe that a routine can be implemented by three weeks of age.

You can start on a daily routine after your milk has come in and you are settled. This is what I call 'Weeks 1 and 2 routine' (see page 148). Each day is different in timing but you are waking and feeding your baby rather than feeding on demand. It has to be flexible though as both of you are learning and of course your baby's growth and well-being is the most important thing. You are beginning by creating a difference between night and day.

How often should I bath my newborn?

It is not necessary to bath a newborn daily; just once or twice a week to begin with, and then every other day. However, if it's an enjoyable experience for you all a daily bath is fine.

feeding your baby

Breastfeeding your baby

Breastfeeding is incredibly special and, eventually, a rewarding experience for you and your baby. To begin with, however, most mothers find it to be quite a challenge: struggling with sore or cracked nipples, babies who don't latch correctly, limited milk supply and blocked milk ducts. It is vital to get the right help from the beginning (from your midwife or a lactation consultant) as once they know what to do, most women do not look back and feeding becomes a joy.

Every woman's breasts are different, some are large, some are small, some have had reconstructive surgery, and some have flat or inverted nipples. Even the nipple angle can be different from one woman to another! Often these subtle differences are the reason why so many women struggle with breastfeeding, as some advice might not be quite right for their particular breast or nipple shape.

Many of the mothers I have helped with latching problems find that once both they and the baby have had some practice breastfeeding becomes second nature. Soon they are able to feed in any old position!

Giving breastfeeding advice in a book is very hard as it is a visual technique and should be tailored to each individual woman, but I have put together basic tips for every breastfeeding mother to bear in mind.

Different positions for feeding your baby

* Across-your-body hold

Position your baby with nose to nipple and tummy to tummy. Turn your baby onto their side and cradle their head in your hand, tucking their body in your arm. Your hand should be guiding their head. When they open their mouth, bring baby to you, instead of you leaning down to baby. If you find that your nipple doesn't face directly in front of you and faces down from the breast or to the side, you will need to adjust your baby's position so that their nose is in line with the breast.

* Underarm hold (rugby hold)

This position of feeding your baby down the side of your body instead of across your body is a good starting position. It can be easier for some in the early days, especially when a mother's milk first comes in. You need to have a pillow for this position to lift the baby to the right height for

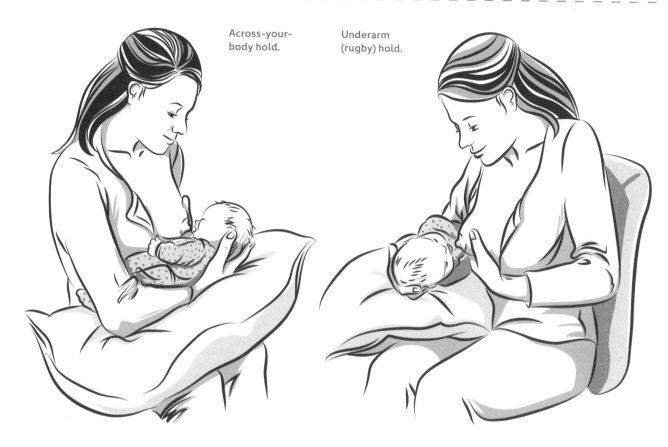

Across-your-body hold.

Underarm (rugby) hold.

you. Mothers with larger breasts or those who find it awkward to bring baby to breast with their left arm (when right-handed) find using this position quite good for a short period of time.

* Lying down

This is a great position for women who have larger breasts or a plentiful milk supply. Just ensure that you have your head in a comfortable position, as your neck can get a little sore if unsupported.

At night you do have to be careful not to fall asleep. In case this happens, I would always encourage a mother to place a pillow behind their baby so they cannot roll off the bed. Setting an alarm near you for the end of a feed is a good idea so you can turn your baby onto their back and position them safely or return them to their own bed.

Posture

Having the correct posture while feeding is vital as you are going to be spending many hours feeding and after some time your neck, shoulders and back will suffer if not supported correctly. Remember to relax your shoulders after latching baby to breast. I suggest mothers follow this sequence:

1. Sit comfortably or lie down with neck well supported.
2. Latch baby to breast.
3. Take a deep breath to help you relax both mentally and physically.

Latching

Tickle or tease your baby with your nipple, stroking their cheek (this activates their rooting reflex and they will open their mouth) or touching their upper lip area. When they open their mouth wide, bring them quickly to the breast. Their lips should cover some or all of your areola area. If the discomfort of the latch has not eased within seconds of the baby latching, you more than likely need to take your baby off (see Removing baby from the breast, page 41) and start again. It is normal for the feed to be slightly uncomfortable but not painful. Seek help if you cannot achieve a comfortable latch.

I find it is best to hold your baby as confidently as possible and, guiding their head, bring baby to the breast in a quick motion when they have their mouth wide open.

Using a shield

The use of a nipple shield is mostly for mothers who have flat or inverted nipples but it is sometimes also recommended when you have cracked nipples as it gives you a little time for them to heal.

Seek advice if you find that you cannot move off the shields; there is no harm in using them long-term but it is a little more work for you and in some cases it doesn't allow your baby to fully drain your breast.

TIPS FOR USING A SHIELD

- If you use a shield to help your baby latch, try taking your baby off the breast after 2–3 minutes and try latching to the breast without the use of the shield. The nipple might have protruded more and the breast should be softening slightly.

- Express after using the shield in the early weeks after the birth and when you feel that your baby may not have drained your breast adequately.

Feeding from one breast or two per feed

Some women are advised in the initial days and weeks of feeding to feed from one breast for one feed time and then from the other at the next feed. While this advice can be correct or helpful for some women, it can be quite detrimental for others as during the 3-, 6- or 9-week growth spurts some babies are hungrier than before and while one breast was sufficient yesterday, today they might like more. Similarly, one breast in the middle of the night or morning might be sufficient but at the end of the day a baby might like both. Possible signs that your baby might need more than what you are offering them are:

- Unsettled after a feed, mouthing and looking for more milk but when you put them back to the same breast (after they have fed for some time, see note on page 40) they don't stay on the breast. Try offering them the other side if you see this.
- Baby starts pulling or wriggling on the breast after feeding for some time.
- Settled in the daytime when they are first born and sleepy, but at night wanting to feed and feed and feed. Feeding well and offering more during the day can help your baby to be more settled at night.
- When you are feeding from both sides at most feeds, it is important that at your next feed you start on the breast that you last fed off. This enables your baby to feed well (babies normally feed with a stronger suck on the first side) from both breasts throughout a 24-hour period and helps to keep your production up. It also helps to prevent blocked milk ducts.

Feeding for a certain length of time

Oh, this is a controversial topic! How long should you feed a baby for? In the 'old' days and when I was training it was quite widely taught that you feed 10 minutes on one side and 10 minutes on the other side.

Since this time I, personally, have seen that this is not quite right as every mother has a different supply of milk, every baby needs a different amount of milk and there is no one-style-fits-all policy.

I have read books that suggest, for example, that you should feed your baby in the first three weeks of their life for 35 minutes each time. When a client with an abundant milk supply tries to follow this they struggle as they can never reach the recommended time due to their baby being satisfied after just five minutes or so. From my years of experience I have formed a common time-guide (see below) that is suitable for most of my clients.

Until your milk comes in:
Let your baby feed for as long as they would like (25–30 minutes per side, as a guideline); this will help to bring your milk in more rapidly than restricted feeding times.

Once your milk is in:
When feeding from one breast per feed: Let your baby feed for as long as they are happy, around 25–30 minutes is the average time for this, but up to 40 minutes is possible. Sometimes your baby will stop after a few minutes or halfway through, needing to be winded and changed. Continue feeding once they are ready.

When you are feeding from both breasts at most feeds: First side: 15–20 minutes down to 8–10 minutes. Second side: 15 minutes down to 5–10 minutes. *NOTE: If you choose to have your baby on a flexible routine at this early age, I would suggest you keep your baby stimulated while on the breast if they are falling asleep. They will often become sleepy on the breast because they are snug and warm against your skin and being comforted by your milk and they tire from the hard work that is sucking. You may need to strip off a layer of their clothing so they are cooler, which will help them feed for a better length of time.*

Unsettled or 'frantic' baby

Some babies can get quite frantic when you are trying to latch them to the breast because they are very hungry or very tired. I often describe what the baby is doing as 'frenzy'; they might have their mouths wide open and the nipple right in front of them but just will not latch. This can be puzzling for mothers as you are latching them the same way that you usually do and, usually, it works every time. In this situation I suggest you:

- Cuddle and calm baby before trying again.
- Try placing a clean finger in their mouth – often this will remind them of what you are trying to get them to do, i.e., to close their mouth and latch.
- Try another feeding position.
- Express, if your breast is very full, either by hand or for a few seconds with a pump to soften the breast and make it a little easier for them to latch to.
- Remove yourself to a quiet room if there is too much noise or distraction for you both.
- Check that you have them on the right routine, if you are waking your baby to feed, and that they have had enough sleep. Conversely, if your baby wakes of their own accord, but it is too early for the routine that you are trying to follow and you make them wait until it is the 'right' time, they often will behave like this. If a baby is hungry when they wake it can be wise to feed them without delay, as they are usually more rested and relaxed when they first wake from a sleep.

Over-feeding

A lot of my clients tell me they have been told you can never over-feed a breastfed baby. But this is not quite right, in my opinion, as I know that it depends on both the baby and a mother's milk supply.

Some babies are active feeders and love to suckle for long periods. Some babies who are windy or who have digestion discomfort (colic or reflux) may want to suck to ease the discomfort even if they are not hungry. While sucking they take in more air, causing more wind and then tiredness.

Some mothers also worry that their baby loses all their milk when they spill after a feed. Often the spill looks more than it really is. If this happens and they have been awake for some time, I suggest you try to settle your baby to bed. If they do not settle and are looking for the breast then offer a top-up while baby is still swaddled and in a quiet and calm room.

Removing baby from the breast

There are times when you will have to break your baby's suction when on the breast due to the latch being incorrect or your baby having fed well from that side and you would like to offer them the other side.

Doing this correctly is important, especially in the early weeks of feeding, as you can hurt yourself if you don't help the baby to release the suction before taking them off.

How to remove baby from the breast

Wait until your baby pauses from sucking then place your little finger (make sure your nail is short) in the corner of their mouth while attached to the breast and push down on the base of your nipple. Your baby still has the nipple in their mouth at this stage and so you are breaking their suction by doing this.

Breastfeeding multiples

While it is more time-consuming and challenging, breastfeeding more than one baby at a time is entirely possible.

You may be able to produce enough milk for your babies but it is still advisable you talk with a lactation consultant or someone experienced in feeding twins or triplets as it can help you cope with the demands on your body, especially in the early days when most multiple babies are quite small. They may need topping up with a bottle of expressed milk to help them gain weight, as breastfeeding can be a huge effort for tiny babies, or you may need to supplement them with formula due to the limitations of your milk supply.

Feeding on demand is a challenge for most mothers of multiples. They find they never have time to rest and struggle to get other things done because they are nearly always feeding, if both (or all) babies are waking at different times.

I suggest that you either wake and feed your babies at the same time, or tandem feed (when one baby wakes, you feed them and then wake and feed the other(s) so they feed in succession), which gives you some time before the next feeding session.

Feeding on routine with an active milk supply

Many mothers with an active milk supply find that sticking to a feed, play, sleep routine is difficult as their baby can only cope with small feeds at a time. I do not see any problem with 'split' feeding a baby when this is occurring, offering as much as they want on waking and then offering the rest after a little break, say, 20–30 minutes later.

Try to feed your baby near to but not right on their bedtime as you want to avoid feeding them to sleep and giving them wind when they are tired and ready for bed.

Taking care of your nipples

It doesn't take long for your nipples to get used to their new occupation! The care of them in the early days, however, is key to helping them adjust.

TIPS FOR NIPPLE CARE

- At the end of your feed put a little of your breast milk on your nipple; it has healing benefits.
- Apply a small amount of nipple cream; not too much as this may keep your nipples too moist.
- Leave your nipples to air when possible – don't be in a hurry to cover your breasts after or during a feed.
- Don't use body wash or soap on the nipple area.

WARNING SIGNS FOR BREASTS & TIPS FOR HELPING

- A small patch of redness on the skin of one breast (look under your breast also, not just over the top and to the side) can sometimes indicate that a milk duct is slightly blocked. Feed your baby well off this breast at their next feed or express after you have finished the feed to ensure it has drained well.

- You may have a sore area on your breast. Try massaging this area in gentle downward motions while in the shower, using a little oil to make it more comfortable.

- If you feel like you are getting a cold, feel tired and/or have hot and cold flushes, these are signs of infection. Seek help immediately from your midwife or doctor and rest as much as possible.

- There are several natural remedies that encourage milk production, assist with breast infections or blocked ducts and support a mother's well-being at this time. For example, teas for breastfeeding, or herbal and homeopathic remedies – consult a naturopath or homeopathic practitioner about these.

Cabbage!

Once your milk comes in, try using cold cabbage leaves for your breasts if they feel engorged, sore and hot. This wonder remedy has been used as far back as the 1800s.

I remember the first time I saw cabbage being used by a new mother; it looked like the strangest thing. A few years later when I was helping to care for a man with cancer it was used on his injection site to help reduce the swelling.

One of my clients in the UK went to sleep with cabbage leaves on her breasts and when I walked into the room in the middle of the night to help with the feed, all I could smell was cooked cabbage – hmm, not the most pleasant smell but, boy, it did work wonders!

Savoy cabbage is a great size to fit into most mothers' maternity bras but white cabbage is great also. Place leaves over the breast area for 20–30 minutes only after you have finished feeding. Using it during the day is best and try not to fall asleep with the cabbage still in your bra as it can make your nipple/areola area taste and smell a little funny and make latching your baby to the breast a little hard.

Getting to know your breasts!

Most women today are aware that we need to frequently check our breasts for lumps. I remind mothers that they need to do the same while feeding and they also need to keep an eye out in these early days for redness to the skin of the breast or lumps relating to a blocked or potentially blocked milk duct.

After you have washed and before you put your bra or top on have a look at your breasts, particularly if you are not feeling well, if you have a sore breast or area of the breast. Early detection of a blocked milk duct can save a lot of discomfort and possible mastitis.

NOTE: *If you have a lump that doesn't go away, seek advice from your doctor. While the majority of lumps felt during breastfeeding are related to blocked milk ducts, this is not always the case.*

BREASTFEEDING CHECKLIST

- Drink a glass of water.
- Massage breast to help stimulate the let-down.
- Choose your feeding position: across your body, underarm, etc.
- Hold baby's head in your hand, not too firmly. Position nose to nipple.
- Wait until baby's mouth opens wide like a yawn. To encourage your baby to open their mouth, tickle their cheek with your finger or nipple (rooting reflex).
- Bring baby to breast, not breast to baby; bring baby towards you quickly to avoid missing the opportunity of the wide-open mouth.
- If you have a fast let-down, lean back. Use corner of sofa or lie back in bed with good lower back support.
- If uncomfortable for longer than a few seconds, break baby's suction and try again. The right positioning is important to avoid damaging your nipple.
- Baby's lips should be on the areola area of nipple; some babies will get most of the areola in their mouth, others less, depending on the size of your areola.
- During a feed, if your baby is sleepy and needs encouraging, tickle their cheek gently, touch their feet, talk to them and make sure they are not too warm. Being close to your body provides extra warmth.
- Towards the end of the feed giving gentle compressions or massaging your breast in downwards strokes will help clear the final milk out of the ducts and give baby the last of the rich hindmilk.

Bottle feeding your baby

While I believe that breastfeeding your baby is important, it has been very clear in my career that there is a huge emphasis placed on this, particularly in New Zealand, and often mothers who decide not to or who are unable to breastfeed feel like they have failed as a mother.

In my opinion, 'Happy Mother, Happy Baby' and vice versa. When a baby is settled because they are being fed well, a mother will feel as if she is able to care for her baby. When a mother struggles with guilt or pain, the baby often picks up on this, resulting in unsettled behaviour.

Be strong and confident in your decision and know that we are very lucky today to have infant formulas that have been researched and tested and will meet your baby's needs very well. Bottle feeding can give you a lot of pleasure and the bonding process still takes place because you can look directly at their face while you feed them, holding them close to your body.

Several of my clients have also mentioned that they love to watch their partner or another family member feeding their new baby – an opportunity that a mother doesn't otherwise get to see or a father to experience.

Bottle feeding expressed breast milk (EBM)

There are a number of reasons why you may be looking into giving your baby a bottle with your EBM and we are lucky today to have efficient expressing machines and willing partners or carers to assist in feeding a baby when you need some help.

The majority of families start introducing an EBM bottle when the father wants to become involved or to support a mother if she requires extra rest. The benefits are:

• Fathers can feed if mum is too tired and needs to go to bed early.
• Early introduction can save issues later on when trying to wean baby onto a bottle, especially for mothers who intend to go back to work within a year of their baby's birth.

If you are interested in introducing a daily bottle, I suggest offering it at the Dream Feed time (approximately 10pm) when fathers can feed baby the bottle.

For this purpose you are best to express in the morning (½–1 hour after a feed) to get the fatty stuff (hindmilk) to make baby last longer in the night. You might find they need a little encouragement to establish the sucking action (see Tips on page 47) when you first offer the bottle. It may take a few days or weeks for them to learn the difference between the nipple and the silicone/rubber teat but, as long as you are only offering your baby a bottle occasionally or once a day, there should be no reason for nipple/teat confusion.

To bottle feed, cradle your baby securely in your arm, holding their outside leg in your hand and cradling their head in the crook of your elbow. Their inside arm should be tucked under yours.

Keeping your baby's milk

* Expressed breast milk

Once you have expressed, the milk has to be put in the fridge within the hour. Place it at the back of the fridge, not in the door as the temperature will fluctuate more there. The milk can stay in the fridge for up to five days; if not used in this time, throw it away or freeze it.

If you are not sure when you will use it, put it in a sterile bag or container and freeze it (usually I would freeze any quantity larger than

30 ml). It will last, if stored in its own airtight container at the back or bottom of the freezer, for up to 12 months.

To defrost breast milk either:

1. Take it out the night before and place in the fridge to defrost slowly.
2. Take it out and leave on the bench to defrost (should take 1–2 hours).
3. Take it out and sit it in warm (not boiling) water to defrost. Keep changing the water as it cools if you are in a hurry.

You must NEVER heat milk in boiling water or in the microwave. Boil the kettle then let the water sit for about five minutes before using it to heat the milk.

∗ Infant formula

Making up your baby's formula right on feed time is advised; however, if you have made it in advance you can keep it in the fridge for 24 hours. Once you have made up the formula, I would place it in the fridge until feed time if you are not going to feed your baby from the bottle within the hour. If your baby has not finished their bottle you have to throw away the rest of the milk – it cannot be reheated from cold to hot again.

To avoid wasting formula I suggest you make up a 'top-up' bottle, which contains a small amount of formula, and then make the bottle for the feed slightly smaller than recommended. If your baby finishes the main bottle and is still hungry you can add more from the top-up bottle. I keep the top-up bottle in the fridge and pour it into the bottle I have just used.

TIPS FOR HELPING YOUR BABY FEED FROM A BOTTLE

- Tapping the side or end of the bottle will encourage your baby to suck by causing a vibration in the mouth. Tap until they are sucking, stop the tapping when they have the rhythm established and only tap again when they seem to have stopped (for longer than a breath or two).

- Holding their body weight in your arm (by holding onto their outside leg) and rocking or gently jiggling will distract and comfort them and help to start the sucking motion.

- Stop your movements once the baby is drinking well to encourage feeding in the future without movement.

Sterilising

Bottles, dummies and expressing machines all need to be sterilised during the first three months of a newborn's life. Newborns do have good resistance if they live in a clean environment, but breast milk and infant formula are very fatty and if not removed thoroughly will develop bacteria. Washing, scrubbing and rinsing before sterilising is important.

Different brands of sterilisers have different instructions so make sure you read these before use, as it is important to sterilise correctly.

Microwave, or steam-unit, sterilisers (see page 20) are cost-effective and easy to use. If you do not have one, you have a couple of other options:

1. Wash and place all equipment in a pot big enough for the water to cover all the bottles, etc. Bring to the boil and boil for three minutes. Put lid on and leave to cool or use sterile tongs to remove items and assemble. NOTE: *Some breast pump equipment cannot be sterilised like this. Check manufacturer's instructions first.*
2. Use Milton Sterilising Tablets for a sterilising solution that does not require boiling the water (instructions come on the box).

BOTTLE FEEDING CHECKLIST
(expressed breast milk or formula)

- Never heat breast milk in the microwave. Boil kettle five minutes before feed time and then use that hot (but not boiling) water to heat the bottle.
- Always test the temperature of the milk by putting a few drops on the inside of your wrist before giving the bottle to the baby.
- Hold baby close to your body, tucking their inside arm under yours and holding their outside leg in your hand. Some fathers will find this hard because holding a baby close to their body feels awkward. This is often because a man's body/arm shape is different to a woman's, which has been (cleverly!) designed to cradle a baby. Fathers can try using a pillow to raise the baby up higher and give support.
- Start by holding the baby in an upright position, more upright than you would think (roughly a 40–45 degree angle). The reason for this is because it takes a while for your baby to start rhythmic sucking and if you are using a standard teat (instead of a 'Chu Chu' teat or Calma bottle by Medela – see page 19 for details) then the milk will squirt to the back of their mouth and may make them gag a little. This gagging often scares parents as they think their baby is choking.

- Jiggle gently if they are fussing or wriggling; this is a form of distraction and helps to calm them.
- If you find that your baby is not shutting their mouth around the teat of the bottle or has the bottle in their mouth but is not sucking, place your little finger gently underneath their chin or on their cheek. This often helps to encourage the baby to form a suction as it replicates what happens on the breast, i.e., the chin or cheek resting against the breast.
- Tap the side of the bottle with your middle or ring finger if they need encouragement to start sucking. Stop tapping once they have started and have got a rhythm going.
- Make sure the teat has milk in it at all times to stop babies taking in air. Tip baby back as they near the end of the bottle rather than tipping the bottle up further.
- Stop to burp them if they are wriggling or if they have stopped sucking for more than a breath or two. I would suggest that you stop and wind them halfway through (even if they do not seem to be struggling) once they are having more than 30 ml at a time. If they have too much milk prior to winding, they will often bring up milk with the burp.
- If you find that after stopping to wind your baby they will not go back onto the bottle, I suggest that instead you try winding them after the first 10ml.

Common feeding questions

Is it okay to eat everything when breastfeeding?

I believe that most newborn babies are sensitive to certain foods. By the time they are closer to three months of age they are more tolerant and their digestive systems are maturing. So it is trial and error to start. Keeping a food diary and researching common foods to avoid will help determine what is okay for your baby. Remember, it is not forever, so it's better to start on a basic diet and reintroduce foods as your baby gets more settled and when you are more confident. Seek a health professional's advice if you have concerns

I am having trouble latching my baby to my breast and now I have sore nipples. What can I do?

Sore nipples can make it very hard to feed a baby confidently and a lot of the time when I am helping mothers with breastfeeding I see them move cautiously as they take the baby to the breast.

It is important that the position in which you are trying to latch your baby is suitable for your breast shape and size and the direction in which your nipple faces. If you have quite flat or inverted nipples, it may take some time to learn how to latch efficiently. The use of nipple shields may be necessary in this situation. Expressing by hand or with a breast pump can help in the early days of learning.

You may need to show your baby how to open their mouth wide enough by touching the side of their mouth, cheek or top lip with your finger or nipple a few times.

Check that your baby has not got a tongue-tie (see Glossary, page 166). There are conflicting thoughts about the process of 'clipping' tongue-ties today but I see many families who have had this problem and who have seen great results after seeking further help. I would suggest you ask advice from your doctor or a paediatrician if you suspect your baby is tongue-tied.

Make sure your feeding environment is calm. Limit your visitors during your feeding time unless you feel confident feeding in front of them, or move away to a quiet part of the house so you can relax.

Why does my baby often fall asleep while feeding?
When close to your body your baby can become sleepy and may need to be made a little cooler. Taking a layer of baby's clothing off during a feed ensures they don't get too hot but they still receive warmth from your body.

Sometimes they are simply tired from not having slept long enough.

What can I do to make my milk supply equal my baby's demand?
You may have trouble producing the volume of milk your baby is asking of you! This is not uncommon and there are methods to help increase your supply. (See Milk boosters, page 66.)

Why does my baby gulp and choke a little when having a bottle?
The flow of the teat you are using may be too fast for your small baby. Holding your baby in a more upright position so that they can cope with the continuous flow that most bottles have may help. I suggest you look at another teat/bottle type if the problem continues.

When do babies have their growth spurts?
Babies have a growth spurt at 3, 6 and roughly 9–10 weeks of age. During this time babies will want to feed for longer periods and will probably not last the same amount of time between feeds as they did previously. These growth spurts last for about three days.

If you are following a routine I suggest you try to stick with it, but bear in mind that if your baby is not settling you may need to offer a top-up feed before sleep. You might also find that your routine will be half an hour out of your normal feeding time here and there, but during the growth spurts you need to be flexible.

It is important at this time for you as a mother to increase your intake of food and water to cope with the extra demand on your milk supply. Prepare yourself for this by having easy access to snacks and having evening meals in the freezer for emergencies.

How long should I breastfeed on each breast?

This varies depending on your baby and also on the age and stage they are at. To begin with you will most likely need to feed for long periods, up to 30 minutes say, until the baby's sucking has helped to bring in your milk, changing from just a supply of colostrum.

When your milk comes in (after 3–5 days), you will have very full and sometimes engorged-feeling breasts, so continue to feed for these long periods. Let your baby feed until they have had enough (up to 30 minutes each feed) to relieve the pressure.

When you feel your supply has started to settle down and you feel more comfortable, I suggest you limit your baby to about 15 minutes on each side.

If you want to check your baby has drained your breast sufficiently, you can do so by massaging the breast in downward strokes with your thumbs, then squeezing gently around the areola area (like a baby's latch). You should see milk come to the end of your nipple. Repeat this up to three times. If after the third time you still have a reasonable amount coming out, I would suggest putting your baby back on for another 3–5 minutes. Watch to see that your baby actually sucks when they are back on the breast; if they are a bit slow then do breast compressions to help them.

When is the best time to express in order to build a better milk supply or to have an extra supply in the fridge or freezer?

The best time for expressing is in the mornings, either after the early- or mid-morning feed. Express half an hour to an hour after you have finished the feed.

If your baby takes time to settle then you are best to leave it until after the next feed to ensure you do not express too close to your next feed. (See also Keeping your baby's milk on page 46.)

winding your baby

The practice of winding babies has been around for many years but the importance of it has often been debated. Until I started working as a maternity nurse I did not understand the importance of winding or the impact that wind can have on some babies and their daily well-being.

I learnt after caring for many babies (and many sleepless nights) that the traditional Western way of winding was not enough for small babies: the 'over the shoulder' technique just did not help relieve all the discomfort. With most babies it only brought up the last wind of the feed, not the air bubbles that were created at the beginning of the feed.

There is conflicting advice about winding babies today; some even say that breastfed babies don't need to be winded but bottle-fed babies do! In my opinion, all babies need to be checked for wind.

While working in countries like South Africa, India and Indonesia, I witnessed babies living within extended families; they were carried around, strapped upright to their mother or grandmother for most of the day, fed on demand and often slept on their mother rather than in a bed on their back. If we, in Western countries, lived like this we would not need to spend so much time winding our babies.

I also discovered that most breastfed babies have more wind than bottle-fed babies (breastfed babies have several smaller burps while bottle-fed babies have fewer and larger burps), which made sense of why the 'over the shoulder' technique works for some Western babies (those who were bottle-fed).

A mother's milk flow and baby's sucking strength will impact on how much wind the baby has. Some mothers have a fast milk flow and others slow, meaning some babies will gulp the milk down and others will slowly swallow.

Wind moves through the digestive system with movement and when a baby is lying on their back, therefore, if we do not wind a baby correctly, their wind could move into an uncomfortable spot just when we want them to sleep and prevent them from settling and/or sleeping as well.

As a baby gets stronger, their digestive system matures, and from around 4–6 months of age you do not have to wind a baby as much.

I believe in the 'snowball effect' of wind (see page 61). When a baby's need to be winded is not met it can impact on the rest of the day.

Often unsettled, over-tired or over-stimulated babies are thought to have more wind than they really do and we keep on winding them for long periods of time. This can cause distress for both baby and parent. Confusingly, babies will arch their back or go rigid when distressed (over-tired), just like they do when they actually have wind! What I suggest is that you try for 2–3 burps or winding cycles and if you still have not got any wind up, wrap up your baby and give them a cuddle, rocking or swaying to calm them if necessary. Once you and your baby are calm you will be able to see what they truly need.

So often I see parents who believe their baby is in immense pain when in actual fact they just need to burp, but have become stressed by a parent's worry or by too much stimulation from being over-handled. When I ask the mother if I can help, I take the baby and hold them firmly and confidently over my chest and shoulders, bouncing slightly. The baby will often calm almost immediately and then, if they are still squirming or wriggling, I will try for another burp or offer the baby another feed; the calm sucking can relax them. If you do feed them more at this point and they only want a small top-up, you might not need to wind them again. Just wrap them up, place them in the 'over the shoulder' position and gently tap their back in a heartbeat rhythm. If you have an overactive let-down I suggest you try a dummy, as it can help calm baby before offering the breast, as well as when they are not hungry and just want to suck to relieve discomfort or to help them relax.

Techniques for winding

There is no 'right' way to wind a baby but I have developed technique that has earned me the name 'Burping Queen'! There are three effective ways I use to wind a baby: my technique (a 'sitting up' technique), the classic 'over the shoulder' technique and the 'snuggle burp' technique. All work and have their time and place in a 24-hour day!

When feeding, I would always start with my 'sitting up' technique and then, if you are not having success and have repeated the sequence twice, try the 'over the shoulder' technique.

TIMES TO CHECK FOR WIND

- During a breastfeed and bottle feed (halfway through and more often when you hear them gulping; particularly relevant for those mothers who have very fast milk flow).
- At the end of a feed.
- After lying baby in a flat position: nappy change (even halfway through), play gym, swaddling, etc.
- If you hear a gulping sound when they are lying down. It almost sounds like they are swallowing slightly.

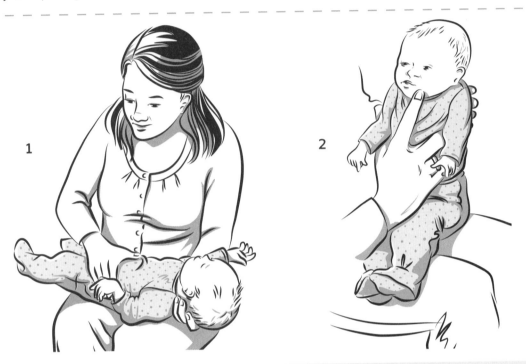

 ## My winding technique

I developed this technique over many years working as a maternity
nurse. It moves the baby in a rhythmic manner to help dislodge the wind
(burps) in their digestive system.

1. As you take your baby off the breast or bottle, lie them flat on their
   back across your knees or beside you on the couch and massage their
   tummy gently two or three times on their nappy line, below the ribs as
   if massaging a knot in someone's shoulder. Repeat this 2–3 times.

2. Place the palm of your hand on your baby's diaphragm area. The tip of
   your index finger and your thumb are supporting their head. Slip your
   other thumb under the inside arm and sit your baby up by lifting them
   up and then down onto your knee to help dislodge the burp. Your other
   hand supports baby's back as you lift. Make sure they are sitting up nice
   and straight with their bottom on (not over) your knee. The palm of your
   hand is sitting low to help lengthen baby's body. Take baby's weight
   with your hands and fingers, and don't allow baby to sink down into
   their hips. The tip of your forefinger supports baby's chin.

3. Gently lift up baby (the head is supported with the shrugging of their
   shoulders) and allow their body to gently dangle for a moment before
   sitting baby back down again. Some babies at this point will bring up

wind without you having to do any tapping on their back. If they bring up one burp, lift them up and then down again; often another will follow.

4. When baby is back in sitting position, 'paddle tap' (a gentle, patting motion) their back between the shoulder blades in a quick, firm rhythm. If you do not get a burp then I would massage each side of their back and then try tapping or lifting them up and down again to stretch out their tummy. If they are grizzly or wriggling in discomfort, gently bounce them at the same time (with your knee).

5. If you hear a liquid-sounding burp, a wet burp, or they spill, lie them almost down across your knees again, keeping their upper body stretched out. This enables the baby to re-swallow or digest the milk without causing discomfort or the hiccups. Tipping them fully back to wipe their face or forward to avoid getting messy only makes it harder for them to swallow the milk back down.

6. Try the 'over the shoulder' technique (see page 56) if you have not yet been successful. Rub their back with upward strokes and pat between the shoulder blades.

7. Once you have the burp up, change their nappy then check for another burp as they have been lying down. (Use the 'over the shoulder' technique.)

8. Offer them the second breast and repeat the process of burping!

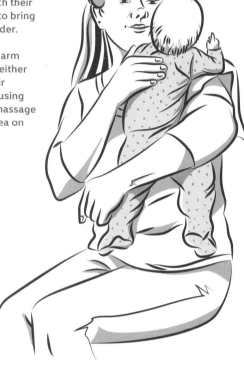

Winding using the classic 'over the shoulder' technique: Lift baby up by placing your hands under their arms. This helps to stretch their body out. Lean forward to bring baby up onto your shoulder.

Next, bring your outside arm across their bottom and either tap their back across their shoulder-blade area or, using upward strokes, gently massage their back and tummy area on either side of their body.

Over the shoulder

This is a pretty easy technique but I do think two things are important to note:

1. Place your arm over their bottom instead of under – this helps to flatten their body out and let the burp travel an easier journey; and
2. When you lift them to your shoulder, place both of your hands under their arms (this makes them shrug their shoulders while supporting their head) and then let their body stretch out as you lift them over your shoulder.

Snuggle burp

This technique is used when they are swaddled. Place them over your shoulder, your arm across their bottom again, but this time I suggest snuggling into their face and neck area at the same time as bouncing slightly to help the burp out. A lovely way to calm and burp at the same time!

Lying your baby flat on their back

Simply lying your baby on a clean floor for a few seconds to enable their body to stretch out will be of great value. The flatter the surface the better for helping a baby's digestive system stretch out.

It is important while learning to wind your baby that you have as much patience as possible. There is plenty of time to practise and if you do not allow enough time for your confidence to build and for your baby to relax in your arms, it will be harder to wind your baby well. No one technique is better than the other, just use what works for you.

NOTE: If you have any concerns about your baby's digestion discomfort or well-being, consult your doctor as some babies may suffer from reflux.

Common winding questions

Does the food that I eat affect the wind my baby has?
I believe so, yes. (See Your breastfeeding diet on page 63.)

Why does my baby seem uncomfortable after feeding?
Sometimes newborns have intolerances or allergies to certain foods so, in my opinion, there are some foods that you should avoid eating as a matter of course while breastfeeding newborn babies.

The frequency and efficiency of winding your baby may need to improve. Winding a baby during and after a breastfeed is vital for most babies.

If your baby is struggling with wind, with latching to the breast and with sleeping, it may be due to positioning in the womb or their delivery. I suggest that you consult a cranial osteopath, alongside advice from your midwife, LMC and doctor.

Often I see babies who are misdiagnosed as being in more discomfort than they really are. In the early years of my career, I used to pace about thinking that baby had very bad wind, tummy discomfort or colic but I soon began to see that over-tiredness, over-stimulation and anxious and tired parents all contribute to a baby's ability to cope with a usual case of wind.

Once you have tried winding your baby two to three times for roughly 3–5 minutes, you know your baby doesn't want any more milk and they have been up for one hour or more, wrap them and cuddle them to calm or put them to bed and try settling them. Take a few deep breaths and even put music on or take a walk if that helps you both to relax. Staying in one room is not advisable if things are not improving.

Some bottle-fed babies may have a teat that is too fast or too slow for them. You may have a very active milk supply that means your newborn baby is gulping and struggling with the flow of your milk. Some mothers produce a lot of fore milk, the first part of the breast milk your baby gets when they latch to the breast. Some feeding positions help with this (see page 36) and there are many things you can do to manage the flow until your baby is able to cope when they are older (see page 42). Patience with winding is essential.

Does flatulence mean I do not have to wind my baby?

Some wind from the baby's digestive system does pass through to the bowel, according to Dr Howard Chilton, Australian author of *Baby on Board*, but not all. In my experience, most babies still do need to be winded after they have passed bowel wind, but probably not as much as normal.

How many burps is enough?

There is no set number of burps a baby has; each feed can be different and each baby is definitely different. The flow of the mother's milk or the flow of the teat of a bottle and, in some cases, the baby's sucking technique will determine how many burps they have. On average, I would say that most babies would have around two to three during a feed and then maybe two to three afterwards. I don't wind the baby constantly to get all these burps up; sometimes they come up while doing a technique or sometimes they come up while you are moving from one position to another, for example, lifting them up after a nappy change.

In cases where a baby is prone to spilling, wind often comes up at the same time.

How can I prevent my baby's hiccups?

The hiccups used to be one of my biggest annoyances when I was a novice maternity nurse. I read book after book and asked many experienced health professionals how to prevent them. The answer was that it was 'normal', babies are not affected by them, and hiccups are due to their immature digestive systems.

This was not the answer I was after and, like many 'normal' things to do with newborns, I discovered only by working with the same age baby for so many years that hiccups occurred in most cases after a breastfeed and when a baby burps and brings milk up with the wind. This often occurs when they are having their nappy changed or when lying on their back on the floor because their digestive system has a chance to stretch out. Because the baby is lying down, when a burp comes up it can bring milk with it, and they have to swallow the milk back down the 'wrong' way, causing hiccups.

Hiccups do not cause pain for most babies and some even find them comforting as they often have them in the womb. However, the babies I see are often kept awake by them or find it hard to latch to the breast if they occur during a feed; it seems to be linked to the baby's personality and whether they are over-tired.

In recent years when I have been helping older babies, a lot of whom have been diagnosed with reflux, I have found a way of helping prevent hiccups by altering the way I wind them and keeping an ear out for the particular wet, gulping sound they make when lying on their back. (See My winding technique [number 5] on page 55.)

We have been advised to see a cranial osteopath to help with our baby's wind. What do you think?
From my years working with babies in the UK, where osteopathy has long been recognised as a valid medical practice, I believe this can be beneficial for babies who suffer from wind or digestion discomfort. Feedback from clients is often that their babies are bringing up wind more easily or, after an unsettled day initially, their baby is sleeping more peacefully. However I do suggest that you see an osteopath experienced in working with babies.

My baby has colic. Is there anything I can do?
Colic in a baby is a very common thing and one that deserves it own section. See My colic story (page 60).

Hiccups do not cause pain for most babies and some even find them comforting as they often have them in the womb. However, the babies I see are often kept awake by them or find it hard to latch to the breast if they occur during a feed

My colic story

Colic has long been regarded as a common problem in new babies, but these days many experts consider colic an over-used and ambiguous term for a range of other 'problems'.

When I first started working with newborn babies around the world I, too, thought that colic was a real problem and struggled to know how best to deal with it. I was supposed to be the 'baby expert' and yet was still pacing up and down with an unsettled baby, sometimes for hours at a time.

When you look up the definition of 'colic' it is most commonly described as a period of time when a baby is unsettled, usually at the end of the day and often for several hours at a time.

As I gained more and more experience with newborns, I learnt some interesting things about colic by trial and error, and because I would not accept that there was nothing I could do to solve this common problem.

I started implementing routines, focusing on feeding, winding and how much sleep a newborn is given throughout the day. I soon discovered that this held the answer! A tired baby who doesn't feed well during the day and hasn't been winded enough won't sleep well and, in turn, won't cope with certain stimulation at the end of the day, resulting in them showing the classic colic signs.

I remember the family in London I was with at the time I made this discovery. Their baby would cry or be unsettled between 6pm and midnight every night unless she was being bounced while walking around or on a Swiss ball, or being walked up and down the stairs! Then, like a light bulb going off, at midnight she would stop crying and settle to sleep. There was a lot of tension in the house between the mother and father. To avoid being caught in the middle, I would take the baby out a lot. This particular baby was a very visual and social baby and, at that time, I did not realise that the outings were very stimulating for her. She was not given the opportunity to be still and sleep. When the situation at home changed, I stopped having to go out quite as much and could create more of a daily routine and the baby became more settled within days.

Stimulation is a huge contributor to a baby being unsettled. Babies are often over-stimulated, which new parents misread as being in pain or still hungry, and then when unsettled they are over-handled. I also believe a mother's milk flow and what she eats when she is breastfeeding influences how settled her baby is.

You can use 'colic drops' to help your baby cope with wind and digestion in the early weeks, especially while you are learning how to wind and forming a good feeding and sleeping routine. These are available from some pharmacies and health stores or from a naturopath.

If you are unsure if your baby is feeding enough or sleeping enough for their age, seek advice from a professional.

'Snowball effect' of colic

Dr Howard Chilton, author of *Baby on Board*, has created a wonderful flowchart which helps to show the vicious cycle, or 'snowball effect' as I call it, of colic. While he doesn't believe in winding babies like I do, we both agree that colic is a term used to describe a baby who suffers from a number of things which normally stem from over-stimulation and lack of sleep. Here is a flowchart of my own devising, showing the 'snowball effect' of colic.

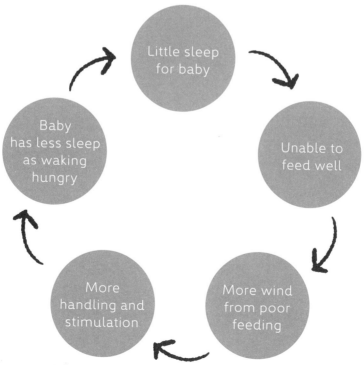

TIPS FOR YOU TO TRY IF YOU THINK YOUR BABY HAS 'COLIC'

If you have any concerns about your baby's well-being you are best to consult your doctor to ensure that there is nothing else that might be causing your baby to be unsettled. Think about the following questions when you are struggling with an unsettled baby.

- Has your baby fed well throughout the day?

- Has your baby slept well?

- Have you been successfully winding your baby at every feed throughout the day?

- Have you eaten something that might have upset your baby? Keeping a food diary will help you identify a common link to unsettled times and foods that you have eaten. (See pages 63–66 for dietary recommendations.)

- Does your baby have 'wide eyes' (see page 81), meaning they may be over-tired?

- Is there a lot going on in the environment you are in that could be stimulating your baby a little too much?

- Have you talked with your doctor about the possibility that your baby has digestion problems other than 'just' the colic (possibly reflux)?

- Does your milk supply appear sufficient at the end of the day?

- Is your baby satisfied on the breast?

- Have you been having enough food, fluids and rest?

your breastfeeding diet

When I was working in the UK the subject of what you can and cannot eat when breastfeeding was quite contentious. Most advice my clients received was that everything was okay in small amounts except alcohol and some medication, of course.

As I was working 24 hours a day, cooking and caring for new mothers and their babies, I saw firsthand the effects of certain foods, in particular the evening meal foods which would become apparent in the middle of the night when the baby was unsettled.

While working in India, I learnt that there, certain foods were avoided while breastfeeding. Before my client was discharged from the hospital in Delhi, a dietician gave her a list of all the foods she should eat to encourage a good milk supply and all the foods to avoid. For example, yellow or white lentils were okay but dark lentils, which have more fibre and are harder to digest, were to be avoided.

The advice I give is quite simple: eat a bare minimum of foods that are acidic or windy (like baked beans or chickpeas – some babies need to avoid these altogether), a small amount of dairy and plenty of the right type of protein. Start by having a simple, wholesome diet and, as your baby settles, after their first 3–6 weeks of life, start introducing more variety and 'test the waters'. You will know within 24 hours if your baby was upset by something you have eaten. It's a case of trial and error.

Interestingly, one of my clients did not have to cut anything from her diet for her first-born but her second-born could not tolerate dairy.

Below are some recommendations and ideas on when and what to eat, how to fit them into your daily routine and things to consider if your baby is suffering from a lot of wind or digestion discomfort. These are my thoughts and opinions, NOT rules! Likewise, the times I suggest are not fixed times you have to stick to, just times that commonly work for families.

Daily diet

Proteins and carbohydrates are the most important food groups followed by vegetables and fruits. Because it takes a lot of energy to produce milk, especially when you are sleep-deprived and running a household or business as well, you need to add more of the above to your diet than what you would have consumed before being pregnant or having the baby. Fluid intake is also important so before every meal and with every breastfeed you should have a glass of water, and more as you need it.

Make sure fruit and vegetables are ripe. The acidity levels in unripe fruit are higher and more likely to upset your baby's tummy.

Suggested daily eating plan

Breakfast: between 6 and 9am

- Porridge*
- Cereals* (choose cereals that do not have too many seeds and raisins)
- Ripe, non-acidic fruit and yoghurt, followed by 2 slices of toast*
- Poached or scrambled eggs and toast (or omelette)
- Buckwheat pancakes with ripe fruit and yoghurt*
- Millet cereal with pear or ripe blueberries and milk*

Morning snack: 9–11am

- Banana**
- Cracker with avocado or cheese*
- Savoury muffin or scone
- Oat slice or muesli bar
- Small handful of almonds
- Protein drink (See Milk boosters, page 66)

Lunch: 12–1.30pm

- Ham sandwich
- Quiche or frittata*
- Leftovers from night before
- Pasta or rice salad with tuna, chicken or tofu
- Cold roast vegetable and lamb salad with almonds and couscous
- Chicken noodle soup
- Teriyaki chicken and rice
- Fruit, such as pear, red apple, ripe stone fruit or melon

Afternoon snack: 2–4pm

- See Morning snack suggestions

Dinner: 6–8pm

- All the good old 'comfort foods', like cottage pie and lasagne*
- Pasta-based meal
- Rice-based meal like risotto or rice with steamed vegetables and tofu
- Roast chicken, kumara and pumpkin with steamed vegetables
- Slow-cooked meal
- Steamed or pan-fried fish with couscous/rice/potatoes/white or yellow lentil patties

* *These foods may have to be altered or eliminated due to their dairy content or foods that babies may have an intolerance of.*

** *A common food that I have witnessed causing mucus build-up in babies. If your baby appears to have a cold or a wheezy chest and you think this may be linked to bananas, try eliminating them from your diet. If symptoms persist, talk with a health professional.*

Foods that may cause wind problems for your baby

I would advise you to talk with a health professional if you have any concerns about your diet and its effect on both you and your baby.

It is important that you don't cut out the foods listed below completely (unless you know there is an allergic reaction to them and you have sought advice), you just need to moderate your intake and trial them. Note down on a daily basis what you eat at each meal and then over a few days or weeks you might see there is a common pattern with your baby when you eat a particular food.

You may read the list below and think, 'Is there anything I CAN eat?' Getting used to a new way of eating can be hard, but if you do change your diet and your baby is more settled you will not look back! Remember it is only for a matter of months (usually only the first 8–12 weeks) when your baby's digestive system is so immature and sensitive.

* Vegetables

All vegetables are high in fibre and so should not be the main ingredient of the meal, rather a portion, but the following cause more problems than others:

- Leeks
- Onions
- Cabbage
- Spinach, broccoli, peas and beans (you are fine to eat these but have smaller portions to begin with)
- Tomatoes
- Garlic

* Fruit

- Kiwifruit
- Grapes
- Oranges
- Banana**
- Unripe fruit – berries and stone fruit

* Other

- Bran flakes
- Wheat
- Lentils (yellow and white are better than red and black) and chickpeas
- Spicy food
- Dairy – this is a hard one as it is very important to have a certain amount for calcium but you may need to look at the quantity you consume throughout a day.

Milk boosters

Your diet and rest (along with feeding your baby regularly) are incredibly important for your milk supply. Below I have listed my favourite 'boosters' for encouraging a good supply and quality of milk.

• Protein drink: If your baby is okay with dairy in your diet, a glass of Complan is great as part of your breakfast or morning/afternoon snack. However, if your baby (or you) suffers from allergies or has an intolerance to dairy there is a great dairy-free protein powder called Pea Protein (it can be ordered from online specialty health stores).
• Goat's rue
• Blessed thistle
• Fenugreek
• Fennel

These are all proven galactagogues and increase lactation and breast milk supply. For further information I suggest you talk with a naturopath or health professional.

Exercising when breastfeeding

Really the only change you need to make when you are exercising after your 6-week check-up is to increase your water, protein and carbohydrate consumption. Your level of exercise will determine how much more you need to consume. Seek advice from a health professional before you start.

I have seen mothers, who do cardio exercise for an hour every day, with unsettled babies and when I checked their milk it revealed that the volume of milk was fine but the quality was not as good due to a low protein and carbohydrate intake. Vegetables and fruit alone are not enough for you when you are breastfeeding!

If you notice that your production of milk is dropping, or the quality of what you express has decreased, then alongside a good, balanced diet you need to consider how much exercise you are doing and how much rest you are getting.

crying and settling

A crying baby, I'm sure every parent will agree, is one of the hardest aspects of parenthood, and not knowing why your baby is crying can be incredibly stressful. However, crying can be a very normal part of a baby's development.

Crying is a baby's best form of communication but can be very hard for some parents to understand and tolerate because they fear that their baby is in pain or that they are harming them in some way by leaving them to cry. It takes time for a parent and baby to learn about each other and during this time there may be a few tears, from both!

A very small amount of complaining or crying when a baby is tired, hungry or in discomfort is normal but not endless minutes, hours, days and nights. Some parents don't believe in leaving a baby to grizzle or cry, while other parents are okay with a little: both may need help in understanding what their baby needs when they are upset. I believe babies who cry for long periods are trying to tell you something. They may have a digestion problem that needs to be dealt with either by winding or by talking with a doctor or health professional; they may be hungry; or it may be you, the parent, who needs help in being shown how to settle your baby.

The 'leave them to cry for 10 minutes' advice is something that I do not believe in mostly, as I find you can settle a baby or teach them to settle by only leaving them for a few minutes, the average time being 1–3 minutes.

I am totally aware, however, that there are times when a parent is really struggling and not coping with trying to get a baby to sleep, that it is best for both baby and parent that you walk away and have time out, leaving the baby to cry for a longer period of time.

If you feel as if you are not coping at all on a daily basis, consult your doctor or talk with a professional, postnatal support group or family: there are solutions to help you.

Common reasons why a baby cries:
- Tiredness
- In need of comfort
- Hunger
- Wind or digestion pain
- Illness
- Teething
- Over-stimulated/not tired enough
- Feeling of uncertainty due to parents' lack of confidence and support
- Lack of consistency and routine

What to try:
- Wrap them up (swaddle) and cuddle to calm them and think about what you are going to do next. It is difficult to think straight when your baby is crying. Offer them the breast or a dummy if you think they might need to suck as this, too, gives you time to think about what else to try.
- Ensure you are winding your newborn baby regularly as this is often the start of all problems. (See Winding your baby on page 52.)
- Learn an effective settling technique that helps to teach your baby to calm and sleep well.
- Learn how long your baby should be awake for at one time.
- Talk with your doctor or health professional to ensure your baby is well.
- Remember to be the parent: babies rely on us to give them comfort and security and if we fear their behaviour they feel more insecure and often cry more.

Settling your baby: 0–3 weeks

Being able to settle your baby to sleep or help a friend or family member with an unsettled baby is probably one of the greatest gifts you can learn.

Babies all need sleep. Some need slightly more sleep than others; some settle more easily than others; and all can be shown how to sleep well, most days – some just need a little more help than others.

After years of working 24 hours a day, six days a week, I soon learnt the importance of sleep! If I did not get enough sleep I struggled to cope with the day-to-day hurdles that can occur with some babies. Just like adults, a baby's ability to cope with daily occurrences is not as great when tired; they may complain or cry more, they may not tolerate wind as well or stimulation at the end of the day.

One of the main 'problems' that I help families with is settling new babies and now, after many years of experience, I believe that all newborn babies' needs are very similar, that they all require roughly the same amount of sleep in their initial weeks of life.

Developmentally and physically, babies can only cope with a limited amount of time awake before needing to sleep, allowing their mind and body to rest and grow. When a baby doesn't get enough sleep in a 24-hour period they struggle to cope with the stimulating environment we live in.

The effects of lack of sleep often 'snowball' and they will not drink or eat enough and then do not sleep long enough due to hunger and, in turn, become over-tired and cannot cope with wind or winding down and sleeping. They can become sensitive and often vulnerable which is sometimes mistaken as being part of their personality.

Advice on how to settle a baby to sleep is vast; parents today are bombarded with many options and opinions on how a baby should sleep and what to do to get them to sleep, often trying everything and anything. What we know is that there is no single way to calm and settle a baby to sleep. Every parent has different beliefs and ideas on how they would like to parent but when nothing seems to be working they need to seek new methods and even think about trying a method that they previously would not have considered.

While I was training in Early Childhood Education I lived with a family who slept their babies in their bed and kept them in the same room as them for quite some years to come. I frequently saw this while working in countries like Indonesia, South Africa and India. No baby bassinets or cots are needed, just a mother who desires to practise this style of parenting, which some call 'natural parenting'.

From what I have seen, 'natural parenting' is a wonderful way of bringing a baby or child up in this world, if you are the right person for it. Some of us are born doers, love to be needed, to help and to mother. Others love to mother but also need to have some time alone or to care for other children, and lack extended family support. While a lot of mothers would like to be 'natural parents', lack of sleep or an unsettled baby may mean they have to look at other parenting styles.

Settling a baby will be different for each family. Many parents do not have the ability or desire to constantly carry, rock or nurse their baby to sleep and seek different ways to settle their baby.

What is most commonly asked of me here in New Zealand is how to settle a baby in a bed, how to have a baby that is happy rather than grizzly and how to teach a baby that sleep is a good thing! Most parents want to learn my methods to help them cope with being a mother and parent, especially if they are living without support.

Parents today are bombarded with many options and opinions on how a baby should sleep and what to do to get them to sleep, often trying everything and anything.

The most common reasons a baby will not settle or sleep well

- Wind discomfort (particularly newborn babies 0–3 months)
- Digestion discomfort or pain, e.g., reflux symptoms
- Growth spurt and feeding problems
- Over-stimulation – out and about a lot, awake for too long
- Too little stimulation – the baby needs to be awake for slightly longer periods as they grow older, but often still show a tired sign at the usual 1-hour mark
- Inconsistent days – no pattern or routine to the day or week
- Settling technique – parents struggle to find a successful settling technique to use on a daily basis
- Temperature – too cold or too hot
- Position when sleeping

How to help your baby settle

It is very important when you are trying to settle a baby that you do not feel like a failure if you cannot calm them. This is a very normal occurrence for new parents, because both you and your baby are learning!

* Wrap and hug

Wrap or swaddle your baby and cuddle them; lay your baby's head on your chest to hear your heartbeat. Remember to take a deep breath and to relax as much as you can so that your baby can feel your confidence. If you are feeling anxious and struggling to relax, take your baby for a walk around the house or garden or pass your baby to your partner or family member or friend.

* Rock or sway

I have watched parents in airports, train stations and on planes rocking, swaying and jiggling a baby when they are trying to calm them or get them to sleep. It just comes naturally. I have caught myself many a time swaying at airports or in a queue at the shops when hearing an unsettled baby! I even once started to rock the buggy with my foot while sitting outside a café

It is very important when you are trying to settle a baby that you do not feel like a failure if you cannot calm them. This is a very normal occurrence for new parents, because both you and your baby are learning!

when I heard a baby cry somewhere nearby. It was not until a man at the next table said to me, 'Excuse me, there is no baby in there!' that I remembered the mother had taken the baby with her inside and had left me with the empty buggy outside! I was just reacting naturally to hearing a baby cry.

In the womb, while a mother is walking around, a baby is very gently rocked inside. This is why a lot of babies will fall asleep when you take them for a walk in a buggy or a ride in the car and why parents often use a hammock as a baby's bed.

The trouble with always using this method of settling is that it is not always possible to do it every time they need to be settled, and at some point the parents will want them to learn to fall asleep on their own.

When choosing to sleep a baby in a bassinet or cot, I usually suggest parents use this method to calm and relax a baby if upset and then, once they are calm, transfer them to their own bed on their side (see Side settling on page 72) and tap or jiggle their bottom to finish them off, as such, so they are actually going to sleep in a still position.

* The dummy

Clients always ask me, 'Is it okay to use a dummy?' Of course it's okay – more than okay sometimes!

I spent many hours when I was starting out as a maternity nurse with families who did not want me to use a dummy and I would find myself with a clean little finger in the baby's mouth (nature's dummy! You need a short nail and to turn your little finger upside down).

Babies might suck their fingers in the womb and, once born, look for that familiar comfort – they are more 'sucky' than those who didn't.

Some believe that if a baby needs to suck you should put them back to the breast to settle them, and this is the perfect thing for some babies if you have a moderate to slow milk flow. If, however, you have a fast flow or let-down, this could make them gag or get wind as they are not hungry and will not suck well. The baby just wants to suck, not feed!

A dummy in this situation is quite handy as you can offer it to them just for a few minutes and then can take it out once they are calm or asleep. I would suggest that during the day you try settling your baby without a dummy but use it as a 'back up'. Use it as something that supports you when other methods don't seem to be working, a tool that can be very helpful when you go out or for those times when you are stuck in traffic or are flying.

Using a dummy will possibly cause some problems in the future, such as your baby waking in the night because the dummy has fallen out. However, they are all habits that you can change when your baby is older and you are more confident at settling.

I like to suggest that you try to wean your baby off the use of a dummy around three months of age or when they find their hands, which is roughly at four months of age, teaching them to settle with the comfort of their fingers or a cuddly, or with my 'supervised settling' technique (see page 97).

Side settling

As I have mentioned before, I do not believe this is the only way of settling a baby but it is a technique that I developed while working with families who chose to teach their babies to settle and be happy in their own bed.

Learning this technique will help to show your baby that their bed is a happy place and that you are always there for them.

The first three weeks of a newborn baby's life should be quite easy for most. It is only when they have problems with weight gain, wind or digestion discomfort that it can be hard. I like to think that in their first three weeks of life you are forming a wonderful bond with each other and that while you are learning about each other you may let your baby fall asleep on you occasionally. However, it can be helpful to use this time when they are mostly just eating and sleeping to introduce the concept of going to sleep in a bed, or sleeping in a bed once they are asleep, if that is what you would like for the future.

A lot of new parents ask me how to settle their baby in a bed and to teach them that it is a happy place they should feel safe and secure in. I believe this process is easier if you start from day one, but just in baby steps.

The World Health Organization and New Zealand's Plunket recommend you sleep a baby on its back in their own bed as the safest position for sleeping. However, in my experience, some babies struggle to settle or sleep in this position, particularly in their initial weeks of life when they can have trouble with wind, stimulation and reflux. From the womb, where they were not lying flat or on their back, it is quite a contrast to suddenly be expected to sleep in this new position.

Often when I teach very tired parents how to settle or sleep their very stressed babies on their side (supported by a rolled hand towel or safety wedge), they come back to tell me what an incredible difference it has made.

To ensure your baby is safe while sleeping on their side, you need to put quite a few things in place first. You will need:
• A clean, if not new, mattress that has been aired and stored in a dry, damp-free place.
• To swaddle your baby for this position, bringing the arm in front of the body so that they cannot roll onto their tummy, like in the recovery position.
• To place a roll or wedge in front of the baby to prevent them rolling onto their tummy.

Before any parent decides to sleep their baby on their side they should seek professional advice. Talk with your doctor about what you would like to do and listen to their thoughts about this practice.

If your baby was born prematurely I would advise you wait until they have reached their 'due' birth date before using this technique (unless otherwise advised by a doctor) as premature babies are more vulnerable when it comes to their sleeping position than those born full term.

The following website has good information on prevention of SIDS (sudden infant death syndrome): http://sids-network.org

My side settling technique

My method uses the rocking or jiggling motion that your baby would get if you were holding them in your arms, but they are in their bed.

- To sleep or settle a baby on their side you need to ensure when swaddling (see page 76) that you have placed their bottom arm in front of their body, not down the side as some purpose-made swaddles are designed for. This helps to prevent them rolling onto their tummy and lying on their arm. Placing a roll or wedge in front of them can prevent them rolling forward too. It should be tucked in front of their tummy area and away from their face.
- Ensure the mattress is flat and it doesn't curl up around your baby's face when tucking them in. There should be nothing near their face. If you have a soft mattress that forms an indentation when your baby sleeps on it, I suggest you turn over the mattress regularly or shake it daily to keep it as flat as possible.
- Turn your baby onto their side, facing away from you. I find if they can't see you and have limited stimulation it enables them to settle better.
- Once they are on their side start a tapping/jiggling motion on their bottom that moves their body gently in the bed, reminding them of the movement they had in the womb. This motion distracts, calms and gives them comfort through touch, which is useful as it means they can be settled anywhere (on a plane or even in a boat like I once did with a toddler!) rather than relying on being rocked in a buggy, bassinet or car.
- Start with a quick heartbeat tap or hands-on vibration, slowing down or increasing speed according to your baby's response.
- Once your baby has calmed or is asleep you can turn them carefully onto their back and leave the room.

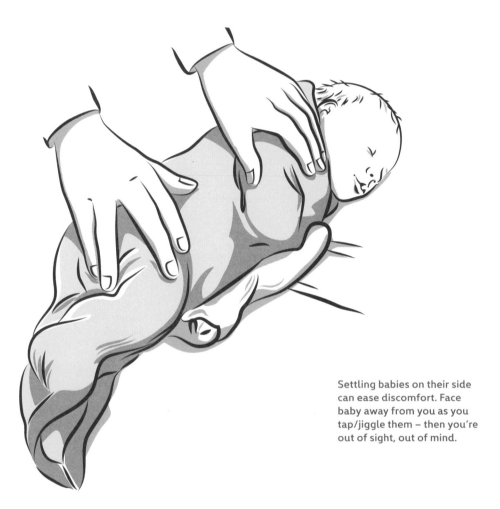

Settling babies on their side can ease discomfort. Face baby away from you as you tap/jiggle them – then you're out of sight, out of mind.

* **What to think about**

As you try to settle the baby with this method, I suggest that you all the while assess and think about the following:

- Did they feed well before they went to bed? Are they mouthing and looking to suck but when you put them to the breast they fall asleep? In this case I might use a dummy to help them calm in conjunction with the bottom tap.
- During the feed did you hear lots of gulping and loud swallowing sounds? Your baby has more wind if you hear these sounds and will also get a false sense of fullness from the wind.
- Did they burp after their feed or play or before you put them down?

Most babies need to be winded several times during and after a breastfeed. If they are still squirming in their bed then there is no point in trying to settle them until you have winded them. So check for a burp quickly and tuck them back into bed.

- Have they been lying flat or almost flat (on a play mat, changing mat or in bed)? The wind will have centralised and so they will need winding again, using the 'over the shoulder' technique.
- Are their eyes wide open and are they over-tired? In this case I would reduce visual stimulation. Check how long your baby has been awake for. An over-tired baby's cry can mislead you to think they are still hungry. Babies will often want to suck when they are over-tired or unsettled.
- Have they still not settled within 15–20 minutes? Offer a top-up feed (still swaddled) for around five minutes if they fed well at their previous feed, and maybe longer if their last feed was small.
- Are they getting very distressed and are you feeling uncomfortable with how things are progressing? If so, pick them up, calm them down and then try again or rock them to sleep and try this technique again the next day or next sleep.

If you have considered all of the above and you are still struggling to settle your baby, follow my Settling checklist on page 77.

Having a routine is essential for this settling technique to be successful. A routine gives parents a rough idea of how long a baby should be awake for, how long they could sleep and how often they need to feed. This will help you manage your own daily routine, whether it be returning to work or travelling to school or playgroup, while still meeting your baby's needs, allowing them time to sleep and have time at home.

Swaddling

Swaddling or wrapping babies has been practised for many years in many countries. Newborn babies are born with the Moro reflex, commonly known as the startle reflex. This is best described as what occurs when your baby gets a fright when they are moved quickly from one position to another, when they hear a sudden sound or when they move through a sleep cycle (see 45-minute sleep cycles on page 105). Swaddling prevents them flailing and waking themselves when this happens. Swaddling is important until they are almost three months old, when they have more control of their movements and their startle reflex is almost gone.

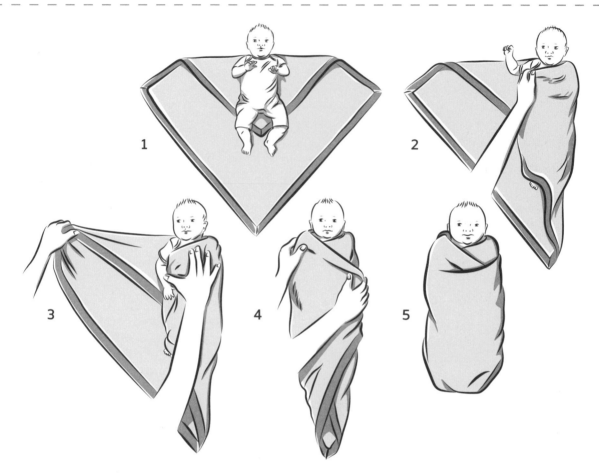

* Swaddling for side settling

1. Gently bring the arm of the side that you will turn them onto across their body on a diagonal. You may need to roll your baby onto that side so you can bring the arm across, as some babies resist this movement when tired. It should be low enough that it cannot pop out the top of the swaddle.

2. Gently hold their arm in place while you bring the wrap across and tuck around their body firmly, still holding that arm in place as it can slip back down the side. The fabric should be about 2–3 cm above their folded arm.

3. Position the second arm down the side of their body and hold it in place with the thumb of your hand that is holding their first arm, while you bring the wrap across firmly and fold it over the elbow of the first arm.

4. When you have the last side of the wrap over the elbow then do a little tuck by pinching a fold of fabric to hold the swaddle in place, and bringing the overhang back up towards baby's shoulder.

5. Tuck remaining fabric under baby's legs.

SETTLING CHECKLIST

- Try to put your baby into bed awake now and then, allowing them to learn to settle in their own bed rather than learning only to fall asleep with you.
- Put baby into bed, on their back or side. Tuck them in and kiss them good night.
- Listen to their complaints. Is it a grizzle or a cry? Is it a consistent sound or more stop-start? At this age only leave your baby if it is a grizzle or a small cry.
- Enter the room, no talking (sound is stimulation), just saying 'shhh'. Turn them onto their side (if not already), putting the roll or wedge in place before you start the settling as follows.
- Place one hand over their upper arm. Your fingers may sit over their swaddled hands if they are wriggling and squirming. Then place your other hand over their bottom area and, without taking your hand off, move their body quickly but gently in a sort of 'shunting' movement. Your aim is to replicate a rocking movement, but in their bed. You start with a quick movement, like a fast heartbeat rhythm, and then slow it down to more of a jiggle or vibration.
- If this movement doesn't work then I would try a heartbeat tap on their bottom, as the vibration and rhythm of it is reassuring to your baby. This is a fairly quick tap similar to what you would do on their back when trying to get wind up. Start with a quick heartbeat rhythm and then slow down to a regular heartbeat speed as they calm.
- Increase and decrease the speed of movement and change the type of the action depending on their mood and reaction to your technique. If the baby is calm and then starts to complain again, increase your speed, slowing down as they start responding to it.
- If they do not respond to your settling within 30–60 seconds I would stop for a little break, sometimes moving away from the bed for a few seconds or even leaving the room before you start your settling again. You can choose at this time to pick your baby up and cuddle them over your shoulder, tapping their back in case they have wind and gently rocking from side to side. If you have picked them up then I suggest you put them back down as soon as they have calmed and try the technique again.
- I would settle them now until they are asleep or until they are calm and lying peacefully. Hold your hands still for around 10 seconds before slowly removing the pressure from them one at a time – don't suddenly remove your hands as it may startle your baby. This is when you would

turn your baby onto their back, if you choose to, or ensure the roll or wedge is in place to prevent them rolling onto their tummy. Tuck them in tightly to make them feel secure.

- It may take three or four attempts to finally settle them when you and your baby are learning to settle to sleep in a bed. Sometimes your baby will go quiet and even close their eyes, but when you leave the room they start grizzling or crying again. Often this is due to being over-tired and it may take longer for them to slip into their deep sleep, which usually takes about five minutes. So when your baby is asleep, just wait patiently with one hand very faintly sitting on their bottom, ready to start a little jiggle if they stir at the 5-minute mark. I find that babies often do a little 'sigh' or twitch just as they go into their deep sleep.
- Leave the room and go back and check on them in another 5–10 minutes, to see if they have gone to sleep or if they are just lying there calmly.
- If you find that they are still awake but happy, after 10–15 minutes I suggest you try to gently settle them again.
- If at any stage in the process you are not having success, then I would rock the bassinet or use a dummy to help them calm and/or cuddle them until they are asleep – this is a new learning process for you both.

Common settling questions

Why is my baby frequently unsettled at the end of the day?
Some know this time as the 'witching hour(s)'. Your baby may be over-tired from lack of sleep in the day or the amount of stimulation they have had.

Your baby may want to feed more frequently than you are offering: a lot of women 'cluster' feed at this time of day due to their milk supply slightly decreasing. Look at feeding your baby more regularly in the morning and midday so that they don't need to 'catch up' as much later in the day.

Make sure you have a rest during the day; your tiredness can affect your ability to be patient at this time. Make sure you're eating well and are drinking plenty of water, too.

A bath in the evening is relaxing for most babies but remember that it is also a form of play or stimulation, so be conscious of how long you are bathing them for at this time of day.

How do I know when my baby is tired?
Babies have a few obvious tired signs – yawning, grizzling or crying, jerky movements or wanting to suck (see page 80). If you notice any of these

and you have finished feeding, look at how long they have been up for and settle them to sleep as soon as possible.

Feeding a baby can take a lot of time in these first three weeks, especially when they are so sleepy or if they have more than one dirty nappy during their feed! Having baby back in bed after one hour awake is the rough goal, but it is important to keep calm and not rush things.

Some babies might only have a small feed and want to go straight back to bed within 30–40 minutes, if they have not slept well beforehand. If they are sleepy and not feeding well and you are struggling to keep them awake, let them sleep. Remember, they are very new to this world. Removing a layer of clothing during a feed can also help to keep them awake.

Why is my baby sleepy during the day and awake at night?
This is quite common and can be changed by waking them to feed regularly during the day and then letting them sleep longer at night. Waking and feeding 2–3 hourly in the day until around 9 or 10pm will help this. After this time I let them sleep (subject to their well-being) until they wake, which is often 3–4 hourly or sometimes more.

I don't believe in the saying 'never wake a sleeping baby' as some babies do need to be guided into a routine during the day that allows you to get more rest in the night, especially when you are coping with more than one child.

How can I settle my baby when we have visitors?
Too many visitors can tire both you and your baby. Monitor the amount of passing around that is happening and give you and your baby time to relax with a cuddle before attempting to put them down to sleep.

Sleeping patterns
As I have mentioned before, I believe that babies all have a similar requirement for sleep and that is why it is possible for a professional to create a routine that most families will be able to follow.

While some parents choose to follow a baby's cues for their sleep times, I believe that some babies need help in knowing when and how to sleep.

Just as you get used to your new baby's sleeping pattern or establish a routine, it is often time to change again as your baby develops so quickly over the first year of life. For example, a lot of people follow the recommendation that a newborn baby be back in bed or asleep within the hour. But as they have frequent growth spurts, particularly during their first three months, this changes. I always aim to increase the time I have kept them awake by roughly 10 minutes if the baby is resisting going to sleep and previously there had been no problem.

Likewise there are families I help who keep their babies up too long, as their baby is a 'wide-eyed' baby who doesn't show obvious tired signs, and then struggle to settle them as they are over-tired.

When I am with a family the first things I find out are how many sleeps their baby has in a day, how old the baby is and how long they are keeping their baby awake for. More often than not, the time they are awake for contributes to the problems they have with sleep. Babies are up either for too long or not long enough, the latter often through fear of having an over-tired baby.

If you are not following a routine but would like to know roughly how long to have your baby up for to avoid over-tiredness, I have given some examples just below. (See also Sleeping patterns and routines on page 146.)

Sleep, feed, play

Usually babies aged 0–3 weeks sleep for 2–3 hours between feeds but they will occasionally sleep for a shorter period, waking hungry. This is an important time for them to gain weight and they need to sleep to be able to feed. If they are feeding on demand, you should wake them 3–4 hourly (subject to what your midwife or LMC has suggested) if they do not wake on their own.

Your baby may sleep for most of the day and only awake for around one hour at a time, which includes their feed and interaction time. You should act on the first tired sign when possible.

Tired signs in newborns

These are pretty easy to understand when you are following a routine because all you have to do is look at the time and think about what you have done previously in the day.

The classic signs are:
• Yawning
• Jerky movements
• Grizzly
• Wired – eyes wide open but they have been up past their normal waking hours (see below).

If your baby yawns when they have just woken from a good sleep or have only been awake for half an hour, they will not be tired (unless unsettled at their previous sleep); they are just yawning after waking from a good, deep sleep. Tired signs are something to look for when it is nearing their sleep time or if they have had an unsettled night or day and you think they might be ready for bed earlier than normal.

Wide eyes

'Wide eyes' is what I call a baby whose eyes are wide open and who is over-tired, 'wired', as such! It is the visual and inquisitive babies who frequently have 'wide eyes'; however, most babies have stages when they are like this.

If you notice that your baby has 'wide eyes' and it is past their bedtime, I would suggest limiting their visual stimulation. Make sure there is not too much for them to look at, such as pictures, soft toys and even the bars on the side of a cot! Secure a plain blanket or something similar over the object if it cannot be removed. Normally a bright bedroom is fine, but at times like this drawing the curtains can help.

Use your index finger to gently stroke over their eyebrows or even softly down their nose. Repeat this slowly but consistently until their eyes start to soften. If your baby does not like being touched like this, while you are tapping their bottom, try placing your hand about 3 cm in front of their face to block their vision. This helps to calm them. An older baby may try to look around your hand but if they are tired enough, and in conjunction with the bottom tap and your perseverance, they should relax and start to close their eyes due to a lack of visual stimulation. NOTE: *If placing your hand in front of them keeps them awake, stop doing it. They should respond to this technique within a minute or two. Either leave the room and come back and try again or keep on tapping and in a few minutes try blocking their vision again.*

> *I have seen mothers who cope quite well with their new sleeping patterns in the first two weeks, but weeks three and four really start to get hard.*

Sleep deprivation

Sleep: we all need it but how much we individually can cope with (or without) varies. I was 24 years old when I started working with babies 24 hours a day, six days a week. Now at 35 years of age I can definitely feel the difference when I have an overnight job. While I am used to getting up in the night, my ability to cope with repetitive nights and running a business is not as good.

I have seen mothers who cope quite well with their new sleeping patterns in the first two weeks, but weeks three and four really start to get hard.

The immense joy having a baby brings will help you through the initial days, when your baby needs to feed regularly, but as things start to settle down your tiredness will set in! Catching up on sleep during the day helps enormously but this is not possible for all new mums and that can make the days and nights a little more challenging.

When I was a maternity nurse, a lot of people said to me, 'Those mums you work for are spoilt. Don't they want to do it on their own?' My response was that the families I was helping were actually very wise and they were fortunate to be able to pay someone to support them through the initial weeks of their baby's life, the time when sleep is most important to help them cope and enjoy their baby. It's just like the 'confinement' time that many Asian countries practise.

These mothers I always 'sent' to bed during the day and it was very interesting because none of the mothers I cared for in the seven years in this job suffered from the same anxiety or the same symptoms, like mastitis, that I see today with some mums doing it alone.

You need to be kind to yourself, allow yourself time to adjust to this new sleeping pattern and, as much as possible, put your feet up. A nap for just 10 minutes is better than having no rest at all during the day.

GROWTH SPURTS

- At particular times in their development the majority of babies will go through a period of 2–3 days where they will be hungrier than before, wanting to feed more frequently. These growth spurts occur roughly at 3, 6, 9 and 15 weeks and 6 months.

- If you have a routine in place, during a growth spurt you will have to be prepared to be flexible as a lot of babies will wake early to be fed or may need a 'top-up' if they are struggling to settle. This is Nature's way of increasing your milk supply when breastfeeding and should not be ignored. If you use a dummy to 'push' your baby out to meet their 'due' feed time you will risk having an unsettled baby or a baby whose weight gain is lower than it could be.

- If you are demand feeding, your baby may need to be fed as frequently as hourly and may appear to be a little fussier on the breast.

Developmental play – the foundation weeks

When a newborn baby arrives into this world, which is bright, noisy and busy, they slowly unfold and adjust, gradually showing us their individual personalities and expressing likes and dislikes about what we put in front of them.

The first six weeks of a newborn's life are particularly important. This is when they are adapting to their new world, learning so much every day through the stimulating and loving environment that is their new home. I like to refer to these early weeks as the 'Foundation Weeks'.

The busy lifestyles many of us lead today can be quite a challenge for some new babies and while you are often advised or encouraged to become involved in group and community classes or activities with your baby, they have their time and place. A baby's personality and a parent's confidence in calming a stimulated baby will determine how much you both can cope with. Amongst others things, stimulation during the first three months of a baby's life can contribute to a baby's being unsettled.

It will take time for you as a parent to adapt to your new role. By spending quiet time with your baby, you will gain confidence and get to know them. This is their first type of 'play', time spent being talked to and being loved by you; they do not need much more than this!

Some babies are born with an ability to cope with a lot more stimulation than others and this is usually quite apparent by three weeks of age! The inquisitive, social babies don't really seem to play the 'sleepy newborn' role, they are wide-eyed and interested from day one.

Parents frequently ask when they should start playing or doing activities with their baby. There is no right or wrong, as you will often hear me say, but from experience I recommend that you steer clear of too much stimulation in these early weeks. Until roughly three weeks of age just lying on a blanket on the floor with or without a nappy on, lying skin-to-skin on mummy or daddy's chest, having a bath or seeing visitors is enough activity.

Bathing your baby

Bathing a baby should be one of the most enjoyable activities of the day. When I started my training, it was the norm to bath babies in shallow, tepid water, in the morning rather than in the evening. However, a Christchurch nurse advocated bathing babies in warm, deep water on their tummies (see photograph page 21), mimicking the conditions of the womb, and brought about a change of approach. Today, most parents bath their babies in warm water and consider it to be an enjoyable experience. The evening bath suits more families, and especially dads, who often will want to be involved in this activity.

However, many parents find their babies cry when bathed. I've found that this is usually due to a baby's tiredness, rather than from the wrong water temperature. When a newborn has not had a lot of sleep or has had a lot of stimulation, a bath can over-stimulate them. They become 'wired', and afterwards are hard to settle. Also babies who suffer from digestion troubles or a lot of wind can sometimes feel uncomfortable if they have had a complete feed before a bath. It's better to give them just a small feed before and then another following their bath.

With the right plan for the day, your baby should float and relax completely through this process. There is a wide variety of bath chairs and tubs to choose from, but the three most important things are having the right temperature, water depth and positioning of your baby in the bath.

Choosing the right time

Newborns are very easily stimulated and so picking the right day and time of day is important. If your baby is very passive or has slept well in the day, they should be okay to have an evening bath, as long it is not too long. (You may need to plan things so you have enough time to manage a feed, a bath and another feed within the recommended awake time for your baby's age.) However, if your baby has been out and about or has not slept well, an evening bath might be too much for them and a morning or afternoon bath would be better. If you have a more active, visual and inquisitive baby, you do have to think carefully before planning the evening's routine as they often become over-stimulated by moving so much when too tired.

I prefer to use a baby bath or big bath without a bath chair so that they have the freedom to float. You can use a bath chair for the washing process or until you gain some confidence, but I would suggest removing it for the end of the bath or when you have the confidence to let them float in deep warm water.

Hold your baby securely by placing your fingers around their outside arm, so their head rests on your wrist.

Bath options

- Baby bath (which sometimes come with a stand)
- Bathing in a basin or sink until too big and then moving on to a bigger bath
- Bath chairs – these can assist by supporting your baby while washing their bodies
- Big bath with older siblings!
- Sharing a bath with a parent – or even a shower (recommended for babies over the age of 6 weeks).

Bath products

Water is the best thing for washing newborns, and I suggest you keep bath products for just once or twice a week as their skin is very delicate and they do not get very dirty. Once babies are moving about more you might like to start using products more frequently.

Around age 2–3 weeks you may notice your baby's skin is peeling and dry. Try putting a little (about 2 drops) olive or grapeseed oil in their bath to help moisturise, but be sure to hold on to them firmly as they are quite slippery!

I recommend using natural products only to avoid any skin irritation caused by chemicals found in most non-organic and bathing products.

However, make sure you do some research as many bath products say they are natural, but even some natural ingredients are not safe for a baby's skin because they may still have harmful 'natural' chemicals in them.

Placing your baby in the bath

Firstly, make sure the bathroom or room you are bathing in is warm and free of draughts. The bath water should be warm (38 degrees Celsius) and quite deep. Once the water is at the required depth, and if using, place a small amount of product in the water (roughly 2 drops). This prevents too many bubbles forming.

As you place your baby into the bath, hold the arm closest to you until they are relaxed and calm, then place a face cloth on their tummy for security (you can stop doing this when you feel your baby is more confident).

First wash their face, starting with their eyes. Use just warm boiled water for the first few weeks to avoid infection and with a muslin or cotton pad wipe from the inside of the eye to the outside, making sure you use a different section of the cloth for each eye (again, to avoid infection).

When washing over their eyebrows make sure you wipe in one direction and then back in the other, to help prevent a build up of dead skin that can form in the eyebrow hair. Continue wiping the rest of their face, across their forehead in circular motions and then around the nostrils and mouth.

Move on to their body, starting under their chin and working down the body. Just use your fingers and thumb to massage the skin clean – they can reach all those difficult places like under arms, under their neck and the creases at the top of their legs.

Lastly, wash their hair. This is done at the end to prevent your baby getting a cold head. Use your hand like a cup to pour over the water and then, using either your fingers or a muslin cloth, massage the scalp in circular motions, using a little pressure but not pushing directly down on the fontanelle area. The circular motions help to prevent a build up of dead skin and reduce the chance of getting cradle cap. NOTE: *Bath every other day until the umbilical cord is off and then it is up to you, every day or every few days.*

Drying

Have the towel lying out flat, ready for you to place on your baby directly out of bath. Wrap them in the towel, sometimes with a quick cuddle to calm them as it is common for babies to get a little upset when taken out of the bath. Towels with hoods are great as they keep their heads warm while the rest of their body is dried.

DRESSING TIP

Once baby is dry, start by putting on their vest as this keeps their chest warm and also helps to calm them if they cry while being dried and dressed. You could also offer a small breastfeed, as often newborns are hungry after a bath and get upset while waiting for the milk. A small breastfeed or a waiting bottle can save a habit forming over unpleasant dressing time. Other ideas are to change the place where they are dressed, e.g. on the floor rather than a change table, or to place a mobile over the changing area.

Start by drying the head and face, using a corner of the towel but keeping your baby's body wrapped, then moving on to the rest of the body. I like to dry with one side of the towel and use the other side to keep the baby's body warm. Make sure to dry under the arms, the rolls under their neck, behind their ears and the creases at the top of their legs – those creases are hard to get to but are important as, if left, they can get smelly and sore.

Massage

When your baby is older (from about 6 weeks old) you can begin giving them a massage after the bath, using lovely oils. The basics can be learned at a baby massage course or from a book and, if done right, babies tend to love it.

BATHING CHECKLIST

- The bath should be roughly 38 degrees Celsius (bath thermometers are available for checking the temperature).
- Run the water deep enough for baby to float in.
- Placing a flannel over their body gives them security.
- Use product sparingly, and use boiled water to clean eyes for the first 2–3 weeks of age. Clean their eyes from the inside corners outwards, using a clean part of the cloth for each wipe.
- To prevent build-up in eyebrows, wipe in both directions.
- Use gentle, circular motions to wash the head, tipping it back to get under the neck when washing or drying.
- Dry thoroughly behind their ears, under their necks and arms and in the creases at the top of their legs to prevent skin becoming sore and weepy.

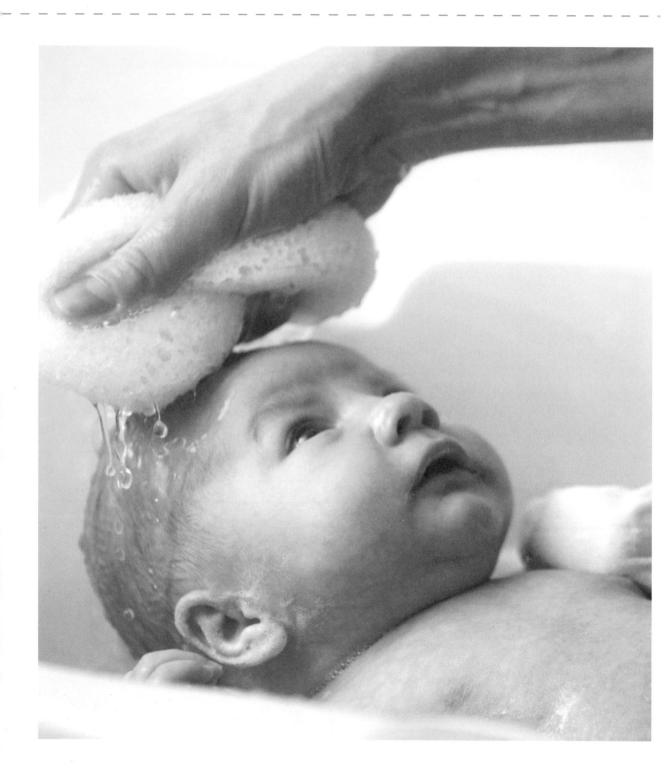

CHAPTER 3

4–6 weeks

Your baby may no longer be the sleepy 'honeymoon period' baby they were to begin with. Remember the majority/minority rule – focus on what you have done well for the majority of the week, not on the few occasions you struggled to settle or wind your baby.

Basic needs: 4–6 weeks

- Bond and take time to communicate with your baby as they become more responsive.
- Limit their awake time – most only cope with 1–1¼ hours.
- Feed frequently – 3–4 hourly or more frequently, particularly at their 6-week growth spurt.
- Limit stimulation – communicating with and responding to you is just the right amount of stimulation for them.
- Have patience when they are feeding and when helping to bring up their wind – winding will get easier as your confidence grows.
- Rest when you can – you will be tired and while you're probably wanting to get out more now, just take it slowly, for both your well-being (milk supply) and your baby's.
- Eat well – this can be hard as you are more tired, but make sure you eat regularly and eat foods that are suitable for your baby's digestion.
- Consider creating a routine – your baby may be showing more personality and expressing their likes or dislikes a little more.
- Have tummy time each day to increase your baby's strength and physical development along with their ability to cope with wind.
- Learn some settling techniques for your not-so-sleepy baby.
- Get out of the house with your newborn for the occasional walk, an outing to a coffee group or to visit family. This is great for helping your baby learn to cope in the wider environment, sleep in a different place and be content wherever you are.

Common questions: 4–6 weeks

Why isn't my baby breastfeeding for as long now?

Your baby will have become more efficient at feeding by now, but still needs to be fed for long periods if a mother's milk supply is good but not abundant. Mothers who have an active milk supply may find their baby is better to be fed small amounts and often. When they have fed for under 10 minutes, for example, baby may need to have a small break, be winded well, nappy changed, cuddled and then be offered more before bedtime. If you don't want your baby to learn to be settled by the breast, I suggest you keep your baby stimulated while feeding by gently touching their feet, hands and body and by talking to them. Falling asleep at the breast occasionally is okay – remember, it's what happens the majority of the time that is important. Be aware, though, that this can give them wind when they are tired, so you will need to check for a burp once or twice before putting them down to bed. Some parents choose to feed their baby to sleep and this, too, is okay.

My breast milk supply seems to be abundant and my baby is gulping in a lot of wind. Should I express before I feed?

While expressing before a feed can be a great idea, particularly to help with the latching process, just watch that you do not over-express. The foremilk (first milk) does have its place; I refer to it as the 'first quencher'. Expressing by hand or with a breast pump for 2–3 minutes should be enough to begin with.

Another method I have used, when helping with twins being tandem fed and whose mother had a very active let-down, was to latch the babies to breast and when (if) the mum felt the let-down we took the babies off, let the milk spray onto a cloth and then, once that slowed down or stopped, we latched the babies back onto the breast. I find that by 10–15 weeks most babies can cope with that first fast let-down.

Look at different positions for feeding that can help to slow down the flow once the baby is latched. Leaning right back or lying down to feed is often the best.

Why does my baby wake hungry after a bottle feed?

If your baby wakes after only a short time asleep but won't increase the amount they take from the bottle, it is probably due to the teat you are using being too slow. There is a very fine line between different teat sizes and too fast causes more trouble than good. The style of the teat could also be the problem. Ask for advice from a professional if you don't know what works best.

Why is my baby struggling with wind?

Your baby may not be able to cope with certain foods in your diet. See page 65 for foods to avoid while breastfeeding.

Winding a baby during and after a breastfeed is still vital for most babies.

Over-tiredness, over-stimulation, and anxious and tired parents all contribute to a baby's ability to cope with a usual level of wind. Once you have tried winding your baby 2–3 times (5 minutes or less), they have had sufficient milk and they have been up for 1–1¼ hours, wrap them and cuddle them until calm or put them to bed and try settling them.

If you still have an active milk supply which causes your baby to gulp or struggle, try a different feeding position (see page 36).

Bottle-fed babies may need to have the teat changed. The flow may be too fast for them or they may now need a teat with a slightly faster flow, especially bigger babies who have quite a strong suck. Sucking hard and gulping can mean they take in more wind. Listen to how much swallowing is happening; gulping may imply the teat is too fast and a little swallowing sound and slow drinking may mean the teat is too slow.

My baby only has a bowel motion every 3–5 days. Is this okay?

Each baby is different. Some babies may not have a dirty nappy for a few days, while others can dirty their nappy at every feed time. I've found that after 2–3 days without a bowel motion some babies can become unsettled and feed poorly. What you eat can affect this, for example, dairy can have a noticeable impact on baby's bowel motions. Always seek advice from a naturopath or doctor if you are concerned or your baby seems unhappy.

What should I do for cradle cap?

Oh, this is my favourite question! What I find best is to put oil (olive or sweet almond) on your baby's scalp about 10 minutes before a bath, then while you are bathing them, add a little warm water to the oil to soften. With a fine-tooth comb or a baby brush gently stimulate their scalp. The oil should soak into the cradle cap and then make it easy to lift off. Avoid or be very careful when brushing over the fontanelle area. If there is quite a bit of cradle cap, do it in little stages (maybe every other day or so). It doesn't hurt a baby when you do this gently, but it may tickle a little or be a weird sensation for them. The skin will look a little red afterwards from being touched but as long as you are gentle it should be okay.

Applying a little oil after you have dried your baby will help to nourish the skin. To prevent cradle cap coming back (and some babies are more prone to this than others), make sure you stimulate their scalp while washing their hair by gently making circular motions with a face cloth or your fingers. Again, be careful over the fontanelle.

Why has my baby started to be hard to settle to sleep in a bed?
Babies are becoming more aware now and they can communicate more;
this may cause you to keep your baby up a little too long as you get
distracted by their gorgeous smile or just by looking at and loving them.

At 4–6 weeks old, your baby has recovered from the birth and is ready
to learn and express how they feel. If they are in pain, over-tired, cold, hot
or hungry, they will let you know how they feel and this might catch you
by surprise, particularly if they were very sleepy for their first three weeks.

A baby who is over-tired will often display the same signs as when they
are in discomfort from wind; make sure you keep an eye on the time and if
your baby has been awake for longer than 1¼ hours, I would swaddle and
cuddle to calm and if that is not working put them to bed, turning them
onto their side (see Swaddling for side settling on page 76), tuck them in
nice and snugly and start my side settling technique (see page 73), or try
rocking the bassinet until they are calm and then finish off with the bottom
tapping. Once asleep you can then turn them onto their back to sleep.

If a baby is showing signs of digestion discomfort or reflux, lying flat on
their back in bed can often be uncomfortable for them. Raise their bed and
use a wedge or a roll to help keep them in place, preventing them rolling to
the bottom of the bed. Talk with your doctor or health professional if your
baby is not happy about being placed on their back to sleep as it may be a
sign your baby has reflux and you need to discuss your options.

A lot of the time I see babies who are spilly become over-tired because
their mothers feed them again, worrying that they have 'lost' all their feed.
I suggest you only top up babies if they are looking to suckle and if they
don't feed well, put them to bed and try to settle them. If, however, they are
not settled within 20 minutes I would offer a breast or bottle top-up again.

Too many visitors can tire both you and your baby, so monitor the amount
of passing around of baby that happens and give you and your baby time to
relax with a cuddle before attempting to put them down to sleep.

**Why is my baby frequently unsettled at the end of the day or in the
early hours of the morning?**
It may be that by now your baby can cope with being awake a little longer
than in their first 3–4 weeks of life if they sleep well in the day and have the
right amount of stimulation (little). Look at increasing their 1-hour awake
time by 15–20 minutes at their bath and feed time, as long as they have
slept well during the day. But as bath time can be stimulating for them, be
aware of how long you are bathing them for.

As in the first three weeks, your baby may want to feed more frequently
than you are offering. Look at feeding your baby more regularly in the

morning and midday so that they don't need to 'catch up' as much at the end of the day. You could also try 'cluster' feeds around this time of day (see Glossary, page 166).

Make sure you get plenty of rest, eat well and drink enough water. What you eat for dinner may come through in the milk you produce at night, so check that what you are eating isn't a wind-causing food (see page 65).

If your baby is unsettled in the early hours of the morning, it may be because your milk supply is so good (due to more rest and a longer period of time between feeds) and therefore your baby may only need to feed from one breast or, if feeding from both, they may need to be winded a little more.

I'm still struggling to catch my baby's tired signs.
Every baby can only cope with a certain amount of stimulation after their feed. Start monitoring how long you are keeping them awake for and reduce it if necessary. (See Sleeping patterns and routines on page 146.)

Keep an eye out for the obvious tired signs – yawning, grizzling or crying, jerky movements or wanting to suck. If you notice any of these and you have finished feeding, look at how long they have been up for (around 1–1¼ hours is generally enough at this age) and settle to sleep.

If your baby hasn't slept well beforehand, they may want to go back to bed within 45 minutes to one hour. If they are struggling to keep awake, let them sleep.

My baby is still sleepy during the day and awake at night. How can I change that?
As in the first three weeks, make sure you are waking them to feed regularly during the day and then, if they want to (and are healthy enough), let them sleep longer at night. Waking and feeding 3–4 hourly in the day until around 9–10pm will help this. After this time I let them sleep as long as they seem well and contented until they wake.

How can I go out without disrupting my baby too much? How do I transfer my baby from the car seat or buggy to bed without waking them?
I would leave the house after they have had time to have a kick, not straight after the feed, as this is when a baby this small will often fall straight back to sleep with the movement of the car or buggy. If you leave the house when it is their 'due' sleep time they are more likely to have a deeper sleep because they have had time awake or playtime. If you are demand feeding your baby, you can go out straight after a feed. They may fall asleep sooner but as long as they are not unsettled later in the day this is okay.

I like to place the baby in the car seat and then, once they are belted in, swaddle the baby's arms away; this helps them to feel safe and to encourage their sleep to be a little longer if you are not in continuous motion. I would always suggest you transfer your baby from a car seat to a flat buggy or pram so that they can sleep soundly (it's also safer). This also helps a baby learn to be moved and resettled.

Try to be home and moving them either side of their sleep cycle. A baby who has been asleep for just 10–20 minutes will be more likely to transfer well at this age than a baby who has been asleep for 35–45 minutes (one sleep cycle). If they resist transferring when you get home, I would offer them a small feed, swaddled, and wind them before putting back to bed. You may need to help them back to sleep with a rock, cuddle, bottom tap or by using my side settling technique (see page 73).

Is it okay to start exercising now? Will it affect my milk supply?
Exercise is important as it improves your mental well-being. 'Happy Mother, Happy Baby'. However, if you are breastfeeding, exercising to lose weight should not be your priority this early on. I suggest walking daily or every few days as the best form of exercise to begin with as it is low impact and will not have too much effect on your milk supply.

Always talk with your midwife or doctor before starting more high-impact exercise, like running. Waiting until after your 6-week check might be the best idea.

Increase your fluid intake when exercising and ensure that your diet is right. You may need to increase your carbohydrates or protein, because while you may have a good quantity of milk, the quality can suffer. Seek professional advice.

Why hasn't my confidence in caring for my baby improved? I feel like I'm not a good mother.
It takes time for every parent to gain confidence. Don't be too hard on yourself, enjoy spending time with your baby and learning about each other. Surround yourself with people who are supportive and whose opinions and ideas on parenting you respect.

Make sure you get as much sleep and rest as possible. It is much easier to cope when you are not exhausted. Remember, there are many parenting courses available in each community and there are also people who will come and help you in your own home, as I do.

Talk with a doctor or health professional about your feelings. It is normal to not have great confidence in the beginning, but you should not feel overwhelmed all the time. Getting on top of these feelings early on will help you enjoy being a mother or parent. Postnatal depression is a very common condition and it should not be taken lightly.

How do I juggle it all? My other child needs more attention and reassurance since bringing the new baby home and I feel guilty for not spending as much time with my new baby as I did with my first.
This is a very common feeling among mothers but, in my opinion, as long as you are meeting their needs regarding feeding, sleeping and comforting, a baby with siblings is often quite happy just watching what you are doing and listening to their older siblings. First-born children will naturally have more time from you as a parent but you should not feel that is the only way of being a parent. Every baby has their position in the family and the experience they have is different, and that is okay.

A new baby in the family can be challenging for older children as they learn how this baby's arrival will impact on them, so it is important to involve them in the day-to-day activities with the baby and encourage their interaction.

Is it okay to start a routine this early?
If you know your baby's development and growth is good then I believe that, with the right advice, you can start a routine at any time. Post three weeks of age is normally when I start a more consistent routine.

The routine you choose has to be flexible though, as both of you are still learning and changing. Most importantly, it has to suit your baby's growth and well-being needs.

Settling your baby: 4–6 weeks

At 4–6 weeks of age your baby has just come out of their 3-week growth spurt and is now heading towards their 6-week one! They are continuing to develop and change, as is their ability to settle.

This 4–6-week-old baby is still very much a newborn, but because they can respond to you more (first smiles and ability to let you know they are not happy about certain things), this is the time I like to start putting practices in place which will help them in the future with things like growth spurts and increased physical and mental stimulation.

Up until now most first-time parents do not leave their babies to complain or cry at all and are still unsure about what they believe on that matter. However, post the 3-week growth spurt, when their babies 'wake up' to the world a little more, a lot of parents ask me how to teach their baby to sleep and settle in a bed without being rocked to sleep.

At this age, I use the same settling technique (see page 73) as when they are first born except I now feel confident in leaving them to complain a little, not necessarily cry (though sometimes a little 1–3 minute cry is enough time to help you figure out what to do) when I know that all their needs have been met. There is a big difference between crying and grizzling but this is not always easy for a new parent to decipher.

A baby is very perceptive to your feelings and when you rush anxiously into their room at the smallest sound, they pick up on your panic. Over a period of time they learn that bed is not a happy place.

When you allow them to grizzle or have a small cry, which I refer to as their settle grizzle (like us tossing and turning to find our comfy spot before going to sleep), you are giving them the opportunity to settle on their own without giving a negative reaction to this sound.

Introduction to 'supervised settling'

When I was working as a maternity nurse I was able to teach mothers over 6–8 weeks, to recognise the sounds a baby makes: a grizzle, a cry for hunger and so on. Now I don't get the luxury of spending as much time with each family and so I have created a guide that a client and I called 'supervised settling'.

Compared with 'controlled crying', 'supervised settling' responds to the sound of (or continuation of) your baby's grizzle and cry, not just strictly timing it to the standard 10 minutes some recommend.

Most babies by this age are really starting to express their personality. While some babies only ever grizzle, others will start crying or even screaming as soon as they are put down to sleep and this can affect a parent's ability to think clearly about what to do.

My 'in and out of the room' supervised settling technique (see opposite page) is a way of showing your baby that you are always there for them but you know, as their parent, that they are tired, that their bed is a safe place and that they need to sleep. You are there to help them but walking away enables you to come back with a fresh look at the situation and it enables a baby to settle on their own after a small complaint. I've found that babies soon learn to feel secure in their bed, with few if any periods of being unsettled, and waking up a very happy baby. You can also use the 'pick up and put down' technique (instead of leaving them to grizzle, you pick them up until they calm down and then put them back in bed and continue with bottom tapping) in conjunction with 'supervised settling' if you wish. With this technique you allow your baby to grizzle but instead of leaving the room, you pick them up and cuddle until calm, putting them back into bed according to the time-guides below.

Unlike other baby advisors who use the 'in and out of the room' settling technique, when I let a baby complain or have a small cry, I leave them for the longest period of time at the beginning and decrease the time I am out of the room if they continue to be upset.

My supervised settling technique

My supervised settling technique is also known as the 'in and out of the room' technique. Below is a guide to help you know when and how to respond to a baby who will not settle alone or who wakes early from a sleep. I recommend that your baby is well fed and has been awake for the recommended time before attempting 'supervised settling'.

As a new parent it can be hard to identify hunger and tired signs, therefore, it is best to have a routine guide and know that your baby is well before you proceed.

First time leaving them to complain: 3–5 minutes (1–2 minutes minimum) of consistent crying and 10–15 minutes (5–8 minutes minimum) of grizzling or inconsistent crying.
1st time in the room: 30–60 seconds, this is just to calm them or to try to calm them! Leave regardless of your success (unless they are unwell).

Second time leaving them to complain: 2–3 minutes of consistent crying and 8–10 minutes of inconsistent crying.
Second time in the room: 2–3 minutes, leaving them once they are calm.
NOTE: If they were over-tired you may spend up to 5 minutes settling.

Third time leaving them to complain: 1–2 minutes of consistent crying and 5 minutes of inconsistent crying.
Third time in the room: 3–5 minutes, settling until asleep or almost asleep. NOTE: At this stage I would offer a top-up for 5 minutes on the breast if they are showing signs of hunger and if they are newborn babies, or you may like to try the dummy if you are sure they have fed well.

If you have to continue, reduce the time you leave the room to 1–2 minutes and spend up to 10–15 minutes settling if they have been quite stressed. If you have still not been able to settle them back to sleep, look at the time; think about whether it is worth still trying to settle them (by this time it may be nearing their usual wake time) or if you should just leave them awake now and try again at their next sleep time. Your routine might run early for the day but that's okay. Don't stress yourself out by the lack of success this time.

If it is the middle of the night, I would only ever attempt settling your baby for up to 30–45 minutes. After this, stop and either top your baby up with milk or cuddle them until calm or asleep.
NOTE: These timings are a guide; you may increase or decrease these times to suit you. If you are not seeing progress within three days, I would think about seeking advice from a health professional.

Swaddling

Now that your baby is getting stronger their arms or hands may escape from their swaddle and this can prevent them settling to sleep or can wake them when going through the light part of their sleep (see 45-minute sleep cycles on page 105).

If this occurs, I suggest you try to re-swaddle your baby while they are in bed rather than getting them out of bed, which can stimulate them and make them hard to settle to sleep.

Doing this as quickly but as calmly as possible is best. I often get parents saying to me, 'Wow, how can you do that so quickly?' It is all patience and practice. It can take quite some time to learn what style of swaddling is best for you and your baby.

You can buy purpose-made swaddles to help keep a baby's arms in and if these work for you that is great, just be aware that most of these swaddles are designed for babies who sleep on their backs. If you choose to settle your baby on their side, you may have to adapt or change the swaddle so your baby's arm is in front of their body, preventing them from lying on their arm or rolling onto their tummy during supervised settling.

Developmental play: 4–6 weeks

Your baby will be responding to your voice and facial movements so much more now. Using different octaves and expressions will capture your baby's interest.

Your baby may smile at you when you are communicating face to face. This is so addictive, their response fills your heart with such joy and it's very hard not to keep seeking that smile or reaction; however, you have to be aware that your baby at this age can still be easily over-stimulated. Watch for your baby losing interest or getting tired by turning away or 'wide eyes' beginning. Your baby might be harder to settle if you push them too far!

Physically, they may be trying to lift their head slightly as their stomach muscles are now developing quite quickly. Slowly their grasp reflex will start to soften and their fingers open up.

Looking back at the many hours of video footage I have taken of these 'first' responses, I see many babies who are given far too many toys or objects to play with. Keep it simple.

Watch for your baby losing interest or getting tired by turning away or 'wide eyes' beginning. Your baby might be harder to settle if you push them too far!

Ideas for brief activity time

* Nappy-free time

Taking your baby's nappy off is not just a thing from the past, when babies needed their bottoms aired due to the use of cloth nappies (which were not as well made as today's cloth nappies), it also helps them move more freely. Nappies, both cloth and disposable, limit the amount of movement a baby has, particularly the ability to lift their legs up (scrunching) or twist from their hip area. This activity helps your baby in their natural progression of developing their gross motor skills.

* Talking with you

A newborn baby's ability to see is limited and the ideal distance to hold your baby while talking to them is the same as from your face to your breast (roughly 25–30 cm): Nature's way of helping a mother and baby bond. This allows your baby to focus on your expressions and start to mimic and respond to your communication.

* Tummy time

Tummy time (lying baby on their stomach) is an important part of a baby's physical development as it strengthens their spine and helps them to prepare for rolling, crawling and then eventually walking. However, your baby's body shape and digestive system will determine how much your baby likes this activity.

Babies who are spilly or who suffer from reflux might be best with a soft pillow or blanket rolled into a long roll placed under their upper body. You will need to support them in this position as they can roll off. Place their arms forward slightly to limit pressure on their digestive area.

You may be advised to give them some tummy time every day but I would suggest you only do it when your baby is settled and once they have had time to digest their milk (which limits the time if your baby is a slower feeder). Sometimes it is best to give them 5 minutes' tummy time before a feed, if they have not woken asking for food immediately! Otherwise, a good time could be halfway through a feed and before a bath.

* Contrasting visual stimulation

The old belief that 'a baby cannot see when they are born' is not quite right! They can see, but their ability to focus is limited to a short distance. They find it easier to focus on bold contrasting colours and patterns.

Place black and white pictures by their changing mat or near them while they have a little kick on the floor, or simply put them in a room with you that has good light. Babies will often try to focus on lights in the ceiling, lamps or natural light from windows as they have come from a dark womb and the light is new and bright! This is why when your visual and inquisitive baby is tired it is a good idea to dull the light to help reduce the stimulation.

CHAPTER 4

7–13 weeks

Your baby is still adapting to this new world and is observing and absorbing new things. It's still important to limit their stimulation and help them learn to be on their own some of the time at this stage.

Basic needs: 7–13 weeks

- Limit time awake still – at this age most babies only cope with 1¼–1½ hours awake for the majority of the day and maybe up to 2 hours at the end of the day if they have slept well in the morning.

- Feed 3–4 hourly or more frequently, particularly near their 9-week growth spurt. (See page 82 for tips.)

- Always put your baby down in a safe place as they are getting stronger by this time and their ability to move (rolling, wriggling, twisting) is increasing.

- Winding is still vital after feeds and becomes easier as their physical development strengthens.

- Your baby is getting stronger, physically and mentally, and their interest in the environment is growing. By now you are able to hold your baby in your arms in a more upright position or in a baby chair due to their neck control (still supported) getting stronger.

- Some babies are showing signs of being able to support their head, but be aware that when a baby of this age gets tired they often will lose this new ability.

- Your baby is now starting to have a little more co-ordination when playing under a baby gym or on a mat. Have at least two opportunities in the day where they have this freedom; this not only helps them to develop physically but also helps them to feel okay about being on their own (meaning not held all the time). Some babies will be attempting to roll, even occasionally doing so.

- Create quiet times in your home (no TV or music) for you and your baby to talk to each other.

- If your baby is distracted while feeding, you may have to turn the TV or music off and find a quiet space.

Common questions

Why does my baby only stay on the breast for the first let-down (5–8 minutes) now?

Often babies can start to be a little fussy on the breast at roughly 8–9 weeks of age, pulling off before they have fed well, and in my experience there are two main reasons for this: their increased interest in their environment; and their lack of patience in waiting for the second or third let-down from a breast because of hunger around their growth spurt.

You can pre-empt this new behaviour by gently starting to sway or rock as you sense your baby is about to pull off or using quiet words such as 'shh' or 'Good boy, stay with me'. It is important you do not force your baby back onto the breast as this can cause a negative reaction and feeding could get worse. Distracting them just before the behaviour starts or as it starts can help 'ride' them through pulling off. Taking a deep breath and relaxing as much as possible will help your let-down happen for your baby; being tense and disappointed in their new behaviour will only discourage positive feeding.

Two other things I try if the movement doesn't work are: tapping their bottom in a slow heartbeat rhythm; and, if your baby does pull off and will not latch back to the breast, turning them from the across hold to the rugby hold (see page 36) – often the baby thinks they are going onto the other breast.

Why is my baby fussy while feeding? Is it reflux?

Your baby may be going through a growth spurt and therefore you need to be patient when the fussing starts. The more you worry about this new behaviour the more your baby will pick up on it and it may prolong the period in which the fussing occurs.

Try to use a little distraction by rocking gently during the feed. Sitting in a quiet room, taking a deep breath and trying to relax during their feed will help your let-down happen, as will a consistent rhythm of sucking. When your baby is fussing and you are tense, it may slow this process down.

It is possible that your baby has reflux if they are also unsettled when lying down or trying to sleep. Talk with your doctor.

My breast milk supply seems to be slowing down now that the feed length has decreased. What can I do to increase my supply?

This can occur over a growth spurt and, in this case, I would suggest you express at the end of a small feed or let your baby feed more frequently (if on routine) for a period of 3–5 days to help increase your supply.

Ensure you are getting enough rest and you are eating well.

Breastfeeding remedies that you can get from a naturopath or health store would be a good support for you during this time.

Why won't my baby take a bottle?
This is because your baby by now is a little surer of what they like and the texture of the teat is very different to the nipple.

Ensure you have the right bottle. I find that bottles with teats that are wide and look like a breast have too much flexibility near the 'nipple' and your baby will just push the teat out with their tongue. (See Introducing a bottle on page 121.)

It may also be that you are trying at the wrong time of day; choosing a time when your baby is sleepy and relaxed is advised.

How long should my baby be sleeping during the day?
The average sleep time for a baby in this period of their development is between 2–2½ hours and as little as 1¾ hours. (See Sleeping patterns and routines on page 146 and Suggested routines on page 148.)

Why was my baby sleeping 1½–2 hours, 2–3 times a day, but now they are only sleeping 45 minutes for some or all of their day sleeps?
This most commonly occurs when you often take your baby out and their sleep is broken; when your baby is fussy feeding and then waking hungry after a sleep cycle despite being still tired; and when your baby can tolerate being kept up for a little longer than before, maybe another 10–15 minutes (trial and error). See 45-minute sleep cycles, page 105 for more on this.

My baby is sleeping well during the day but, while I try to settle them from 7pm, they will not settle to sleep until 8 or 9pm. What can I do?
This could be because your baby is not quite tired enough when you try to put them down in the evening, especially those babies who sleep well throughout the day. Or your baby could be hungry; a mother's milk supply can sometimes be a little less fatty in the afternoon and so they need to be fed more often at this time so they can settle at night.

By now babies have roughly a 12–13-hour day cycle, so if they start the day at 7am (meaning your baby has a quiet playtime or awake time after their feed at 7am instead of going straight back to bed), they will be ready to settle to sleep at 7–8pm. If you start your day at 8am they are more likely to be ready to go to sleep at 8–9pm. Whatever time you choose to start your day is up to you, but be aware that the later your baby wakes, the later they will go into deep sleep at night.

How do I go out without disrupting my baby too much? When I get home my baby won't transfer from the car seat or buggy to bed without waking.
This is very common. If you are feeding on demand and your baby is happy with this disruption, just try to limit the number of times you go out in a week. (See page 93 for suggestions on how to cope with this.)

If your baby is very unsettled in the afternoon/evening after going out during the day, it may be due to this daytime sleep disruption. I suggest you try to only transfer them either side of their sleep cycle or you only stop your movement when they are due for their next feed, timing your movements to suit your baby and not just when you decide!

Learning how to transfer and how to sleep in different environments is a positive thing for your baby, but the personality of your baby will determine how often you do can do it. If you have a visual and inquisitive baby, transferring or sleeping in new and different environments may be a little harder.

How do I transition my baby from their bassinet to a cot?

This is actually a harder process for a mother or parent than it is for most babies! What I normally suggest you do is start by sleeping your baby in their cot during the day and if that goes well then carry it over to the night sleep. If your baby has been sleeping in your room and moving them to a cot means you have to put them in their own room, I would just wean them off by having day sleeps in the new room and then their night sleeps in your room. Once you see that your baby is happy in their new cot or room, you will feel more confident about sleeping them in there at night. If you are worried, try to see if you can fit the cot into your room until both you and your baby are happy.

If the cot mattress is firmer than the bassinet, put a softer layer (like a wool blanket or sheepskin) underneath the fitted cot sheet. The other thing I try sometimes is putting the bassinet mattress in the cot, making sure your baby cannot roll off by placing a rolled-up hand towel or a wedge either side of your baby.

Settling your baby: 7–13 weeks

A 7–13-week-old baby is getting stronger and with this their ability to resist being settled may increase. I use the same settling technique with babies at this stage as with the 4–6-week-old baby (see page 97) but remind clients to think about their daily patterns and ensure that they have adapted their day in accordance with their baby's personality, growth and well-being.

At the beginning of this stage your baby is moving out of one growth spurt (at 6 weeks) and heading towards the next (at around 9 weeks) so you do have to be gentle and mindful of these periods of change.

At this time, as I have mentioned earlier, babies can start to be a little fussy on the breast or bottle and more interested in what is going on around them than before. This can result in mothers, particularly, getting confused as to whether their baby has had enough to drink or whether they are grizzly due to being tired. If you are struggling to settle a baby and you are unsure if it is due to hunger, offer your baby a top-up and put them back to bed, attempting to settle them again.

There is no problem with using a variety of settling techniques during this time but try to use one more consistently than others as this will help your baby feel more secure and they thrive on repetition.

45-minute sleep cycles

This is a hot topic! For most babies a sleep cycle is around 45 minutes, but for some it is as little as 30 minutes.

Many families request my opinion on why their baby has suddenly started sleeping for just one sleep cycle. Some families and babies are happy with and able to cope with this change of pattern, while others struggle to have the content baby they used to have. This in turn can leave a mum feeling tired and frustrated about what to do with this baby who just isn't sleeping for as long as they feel their baby requires.

Helping parents understand why their baby has started to wake and determining if this is okay for their individual baby is a common part of my job now. There are some babies, those who are either placid or who are on the move a lot in car seats or buggies, who can cope with only one sleep cycle, but the majority of babies need more sleep to be the happiest they can be.

For the majority of my clients' babies, waking after one sleep cycle starts between 7 and 9 weeks of age when a few changes are happening in their life:

- They are becoming more aware and it is very hard to know how long they should be awake for, thus they can be easily over-stimulated which often encourages fitful sleep.
- You have not increased your baby's time awake. When they show you a tired sign you act on it as you did during their first weeks of life, and while they may settle well they are just not quite tired enough to sleep through the sleep cycle.
- You are feeling a little more human again as a mother and normally have increased your activities, which might interrupt your baby's sleep.
- You might have started to think about losing some 'baby weight' and have increased your exercise and started to eat a little less (this can lead to poor milk quality).
- You may have stopped swaddling your baby as you might think they don't like it anymore.

• If your baby is inquisitive and sensitive to noise, you may need to have some 'white noise' on to help create a consistent background noise. Sudden sounds, like the phone or a door knock, can wake them during the light part of their sleep.

The 'snowball effect' of lack of sleep is huge: often the baby will not feed well (frenzy feeding), cannot cope with much stimulation and, then, has another short sleep.

In my experience, it is all about creating a routine that suits you and your baby, having a consistent pattern to your day (for the majority of the week) and thinking about your baby's needs as much as your own – they are developing and growing so much and they need time to sleep.

When you start to notice your baby waking after one sleep cycle, it is important to rule out a few things first: could they be hungry (maybe going through a growth spurt); have they been awake for the recommended length of time; and have you kept them up too long and are they over-tired?

When you have found out how long your baby should be awake for and how long they should be sleeping for (see page 146) you can start the process of resettling.

Resettling a baby can be hard. It is important that you learn a technique that suits you and that you are patient while implementing it as it often takes 3–5 days to change habits. Your baby relies on consistency and repetition to learn how to sleep for longer.

Remember to 'pick your battles'. Don't be too hard on yourself and if you cannot resettle your baby in their bed all the time, choose another option, like walking them in the buggy or putting them in the front pack. The most important thing is that you are happy as then your baby will be too!

Travelling with your baby

Travelling with a baby can be quite a daunting prospect, which I am well aware of having travelled a lot with families during my career as a maternity nurse.

The family I worked for in India asked if I was happy to go with them to Kashmir when their baby was 3 weeks old. They thought it would be a good chance to see how I did things and how to cope with and care for a baby when travelling on a plane, in taxis and while staying in different accommodation.

While I believe that for the majority of the time a baby should be given the opportunity to settle into their new world by staying home and their parents concentrating on bonding and establishing good feeding practices, if you are confident and well organised, occasional travel is okay.

Once when I travelled to the US with a family and their 9-week-old baby, we arrived at their place in Texas to find that the portable cot they had ordered had not arrived. I looked at my options: drawers to sleep the baby in were too small and my single bed was too skinny. The next best thing was to sleep the baby on his back in my empty suitcase, using a changing mat and wool blanket to make it more comfortable!

The essential thing when travelling is to be organised. Plan ahead of time and cover all the possibilities, like what to do if your baby wets their clothes or gets sick, if there are delays on planes (if bottle feeding your baby you will need to travel with more milk than may be needed) and traffic jams.

Travelling tips and advice

* By car

It is recommended that newborn babies (during the first 3 months) should spend as little time as possible in their car seat. Talk with your doctor or health professional about the latest research and information on newborns and car seats.

If you are travelling a long distance with a newborn in a rear-facing car seat, I would advise you to sit in the back with your baby or, if travelling alone, buy a baby rear-view mirror for safely watching your baby while driving.

Make sure your car seat is fitted securely and your baby is not dressed too warmly for the confined space of a car seat.

Use a sunshade on your baby's window if the sun is shining on them.

* By plane

Book a bulkhead seat on the plane well ahead of time to ensure you get a baby bassinet for your journey, or arrive early at the airport if a pre-booking cannot be made.

Use a front pack or sling for carrying your baby around as makes it much easier when carrying bags and handling passports.

While flying, swaddle and sleep your baby as you normally would and they should be quite happy with the constant noise and vibration of the plane. Take an extra flat cloth nappy for using as a sheet in the bassinet on board.

Take a dummy (and a spare) to use for take-off and landing if your baby is not ready for a feed. (Trying to feed a baby who is not hungry can cause them distress.) Sucking and swallowing during take-off and landing will help ease the pressure on their ears.

Have a change of clothes for yourself as altitude can cause your baby to spill more than normal and the confined space can make it difficult for you to eat or feed your baby without making a mess!

Departure time

If you are travelling by car, plan your departure time to best suit your baby's routine. If you have a long journey ahead of you, leaving at night after their bath and evening feed can make for a peaceful trip, as it is their sleep time. If you are tired, however, I would advise leaving in the morning when you are at your best and your baby is due for a morning sleep.

When travelling by plane, try to book a flight to best suit your baby's routine. Long distance journeys by plane are best to be started at night

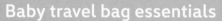

Baby travel bag essentials

- Nappies – always take 3 more nappies than you normally require
- Nappy changing mat or flat cloth nappy – good to keep baby off public surfaces
- Wipes
- Nappy rash cream
- Plastic or storage bag for dirty nappy or clothes
- 2 cloth nappies or cotton cloths·
- Swaddle/blanket – this can be used to drape over your shoulder if feeding in public.
- Alternatively, a pashmina or large merino wrap for covering up while breastfeeding and is also great if cold
- 1–2 changes of clothes, include a warm cardigan, socks or booties and a hat

- Hand sanitiser or soap
- Formula and bottle(s) of cooled, boiled water (if formula fed)
- Bib
- Burp cloth/cloth nappy
- Dummy (plus a spare)
- Toy – plastic rings and/or a toy that makes a small noise is a great distraction
- Calpol or Pamol and a syringe (talk with your doctor about using this medication)
- Front pack or sling
- Snack for breastfeeding mothers – protein bars are a great idea
- Rescue Remedy for you (talk with a naturopath about remedies that might help during your journey)

with older babies as this gives you a good start with sleep, when your baby is due for their longest sleep anyway.

* Stay calm

As you know, babies pick up on how you, as parents, are feeling and if you are stressed or worried about the journey your baby will more than likely sense it and react to it. If you are anxious and you are travelling with your partner or someone else, hand your baby to them – this was often my role when travelling as a maternity nurse!

When you are flying there are always people who can help you or who have been in your position before and most understand exactly what you are feeling!

Developmental play: 7–13 weeks

At the beginning of this stage your baby will be communicating more, making sounds like 'Arrh goo'. I like to encourage this communication by mimicking the sounds they make, mixing it with your usual tone and words.

When I was working in Russia I was amazed to hear the grandmother talking with her grandson (in Russian) and using the same sounds, like 'Arrh goo'! Naïvely, I presumed that these sounds were only made by babies from English-speaking countries, but in fact all babies around the world make these same sounds and don't start practising the sounds of a particular language until they are 5–6 months of age.

Your baby's physical progression is subtle; their grasp reflex will be lessening and they will be able to bring their hands together in the middle of their body, which is the precursor of being able to bring their hands to their mouth or to grasp a toy. They may be able to hold a small object like a rattle for very small periods of time or reach for objects hanging above them when under a baby gym.

Physically your baby will be able to sit well in a baby chair and when sitting or propped up on a pillow safely will be able to follow you with their eyes as you move about the room. They have the ability to follow you for longer distances now, particularly if your movements are slow. They may even start to 'call' out for you with little sounds or the beginnings of laughter when you do something amusing to them. When you respond you will often get an immediate lovely reaction (smile, gurgle), which is a sure sign that you are more in tune with each other now.

Their time awake now has increased and gives you more time together to 'play' and learn. Little outings are more manageable and they can cope with a slight increase in their daily stimulation.

Towards the end of this stage the personality of your baby is really becoming apparent and you both are starting to understand each other a lot more. Your baby recognises you as their parent; particularly their mother, who in most cases is with them for the majority of the day.

I have found that, at this age, babies who have been in the company of adults whom you trust will be more social and trusting of others in the coming months.

Ideas to add to brief activity time

* Singing and movement

Because singing makes your voice change in tone, a baby's interest is captured. To bring a different dimension to this activity use your hands to create movement. Babies will be able to follow your hands with their eyes at this age if you keep your movement slow.

It's not necessary to know all the words to a song, your baby will love to listen to you humming or making up words to a rhythm or tune you are familiar with.

* Mirror play

Babies at this age are fascinated by what they see in the mirror. Even at a younger age babies will look and stare at this interesting object in the mirror, but by now it will hold their interest for longer periods, which encourages tummy time and floor play. I like to use a big mirror rather than just a small one like those attached to some baby gyms, but any mirror is fine. If you are using a big, full length mirror, lean it up against the sofa or a table and make sure it is safely secured.

* Baby massage

Babies love to be touched and by now they will not feel quite so fragile to you and their ability to relax while you massage them should be more apparent. Massage is an ancient practice in Eastern countries and in many tropical islands, which in more recent years has been adopted by the Western world. It is not only a great form of bonding but also with the right education you can learn to help your baby with digestion discomfort or to relax into deeper sleeping patterns. Many courses are available to learn this wonderful and very rewarding skill.

* Outside play

This activity really stimulates all your baby's senses; they can smell, hear and feel the difference between being indoors and outdoors.

In my old Plunket Book from 1977, it states in their routine recommendation that you should place your baby outside in their pram to sleep for a period of time each day and that fresh air is good for your baby! Well, they were not wrong but just sleeping is not optimising the learning time they can have when outside.

Hold your baby over the grass; allow their toes to touch the grass for short periods of time as it can be quite tickly to their sensitive feet; or place a rug under a tree that provides shade from the sun so they can watch the leaves move in the breeze.

Stop talking at times to let them listen to the birds and sounds of the outdoors. If you are talking with another adult or on your phone, move away so your baby has a chance to think about what they are experiencing.

* Naked play

Instead of just nappy-free time have 'naked time'! Babies love to discover their own bodies, the feeling of different things on their skin and the freedom of movement.

During winter, naked play is best in a room that has natural warmth from the sun or in a heated room before or after a bath. Make sure your baby is safe from the sun and away from draughts, particularly in wooden-floored homes.

* Story time

Babies by now have enough concentration skills for you to be able to read a book with them. Of course you can read to a baby prior to this age but by now if you point to the pictures and use animation in your voice they will actually follow with their eyes, reach out for the book to touch and possibly taste it.

Choose books with only a few words, interesting pictures and big, bright and contrasting colours. If you have a book that has wonderful pictures but a lot of words, just make up your own story or point to pictures and tell your baby what they are seeing.

Hold your baby over the grass; allow their toes to touch the grass; or place a rug under a tree that provides shade from the sun so they can watch the leaves move in the breeze.

CHAPTER 5

4–6 months

At this time your baby is going through many changes relating to feeding, sleeping and physical ability. You may have noticed your baby is beginning to have some expectations about familiar daily routines and activities – and becoming frustrated or upset if these are not met!

Basic needs: 4–6 months

- Your baby is going through a transition phase in their development and their daily sleeping pattern may be changing.

- Most babies will be ready for solid food at some stage in the next 2 months. Keeping an eye on their hungry signs or talking with a health professional will help guide you through this new step. (See Introducing solid food on page 124.)

- Your baby will be starting to move, roll, even pushing themselves up into a crawling position. Allowing them time on the floor without restrictive clothing will help them to discover their agility.

- Their milk feeds are still 3–4 hourly during the day but at night they have the ability to sleep for longer periods, some for up to 6–8 hours or longer. This is not the 'rule' however. (See Night waking on page 119.)

- Their ability to cope with wind should be much improved and you may not have to spend as much time winding as you did in the past.

- The time is right to introduce a few more activities in their week, as their ability to stay awake increases, along with their inquisitive, quick-learning nature.

Common questions

Why is my baby still waking in the night? When will he be able to sleep from 7pm–7am?

Not every baby will have the ability to sleep for 12 hours at this age; some can but the majority cannot, either needing a dream feed or one in the middle of the night until they are ready for solid food and are having 1–2 meals a day.

It may be that their daytime routine needs to be adjusted so they do not have too much sleep in the day. (See Stage 3 Daily Routine on page 158.)

When is it okay to start solids?

I believe that the majority of babies are ready sometime between 4 and 6 months of age. However, you should follow your baby's signs rather than starting solids just because you want your baby to sleep longer at night or because you have been told to by friends or family. (See Introducing solid food on page 124.)

Some babies are not ready until after 6 months of age and if by 7–8 months your baby is still not interested, I would look at how many breastfeeds they are having in a 24-hour period. It may be that they are feeding too often for their age.

Why is my baby only sleeping for 45 minutes for every day sleep?

This is very common at this age and normally is linked with their daytime routine: the time they are awake for and how many times you are disrupting their sleep due to being out and about. (See 45-minute sleep cycles on page 105.) It may be that your baby is waking because they are hungry. You can try offering a quick top-up on the breast and putting them back down to bed until you have had a chance to adjust their daily routine or introduce solids.

How many sleeps a day should my baby be having?

This depends on whether you choose to follow a routine or not. If you are demand feeding and you choose to let your baby have shorter sleeps (roughly 45 minutes) then they will probably be having four sleeps a day. Some babies fed on demand will put themselves into a routine and will sleep longer than 45 minutes, sleeping then three times a day.

On routine, I would put a baby down for three sleeps a day. You will need to look at reducing how long your baby sleeps in the afternoon as this might have an impact on going to sleep or staying asleep in the evening. (See Sleeping patterns and routines on page 142 and Stage 3 Daily Routine on page 158.)

My baby is not showing any signs of rolling or crawling. Is this okay?
There are some babies who are more interested in using their fine motor skills rather than their gross motor skills. They watch what is going on around them rather than trying to be part of it or reaching out to touch it! Make sure you are giving your baby the opportunity to move freely on the floor, however. If you are concerned, talk with your doctor or health professional.

Do I still need to wind my baby as frequently as before?
Some babies are still unable to bring their wind up at this age, particularly those who may have reflux symptoms. If your baby can't settle to sleep and burps when picked up, continue with your winding technique and ensure that you give your baby time to play on the floor after their feed as this will help to move the wind through their digestive system. It may be that your baby is not tolerating something you are eating or the formula you are using. Seek advice if you are uncertain.

Why does my baby cry when I leave the room or if someone else picks him up for a cuddle?
Most babies go through what is commonly known as 'separation anxiety' at 7 months, but some start a little earlier. Letting your baby know you are not far away will help. While they are playing and you are moving about the house, tell them where you are, call out to them if you hear them asking for you – 'I'm here. Mummy is coming soon.'
 When a person approaches your baby for a cuddle, warn them that your baby needs time to adjust to their presence and will more than likely be happy to be cuddled if they give them time.

I have to go back to work and my baby will not take a bottle. What can I do?
This is a very common problem. Ensuring you have the best bottle for your baby and allowing them time to adjust is important. (See Introducing a bottle on page 121.)

There are a lot of activities that I would like to take my baby to. Which ones would you advise?
There is no right or wrong activity to do with your baby, you just have to work out what best suits them. The time of day the activities are on is important to ensure your baby is not tired when you go out.
 My choices at this age would be: music and movement groups, like Mainly Music, swimming, Playcentre and coffee group mornings.

I have tried to stop swaddling my baby but now he won't self-settle and wakes after a short sleep cycle. What should I do?
You have to gradually wean your baby off being swaddled as going 'cold turkey' can leave a baby feeling confused by their new freedom. Most babies have lost their startle reflex at 3 months of age and so don't need to be swaddled any longer. (See Weaning off being swaddled on page 120.)

Settling your baby: 4–6 months

At 4–6 months of age your baby is no longer a newborn and with this next stage in their development they are becoming very active and expressive of their likes and dislikes. As your baby transitions into this next stage you may have to re-teach them how to settle and they may start resisting your previous successful methods, like my side settling technique.

I find most of my clients with babies at this age struggle because of their baby's new-found activeness, and often the attempts they make to settle become a battle and not a process that is nice for either party.

If your baby is having settling issues at this age, it is normally due to a change in or implementation of a routine, being over-tired from outings or due to illness and teething. They are also more determined now and changing habits is harder work for you both.

When a baby is able to roll from their back to their tummy and can push themselves up with their arms, I will usually settle them on their tummy and not on their side. I will always try side settling first, if it's been used in the past or if I am meeting a baby for the first time, but it will quickly be very obvious whether it will work or not, just by seeing what the baby is doing physically. If they are kicking and twisting away from you, fighting or resisting, then I would turn them onto their tummy and begin the same 'shhh' and tap on their bottom as I recommend when they are smaller.

The problem with tummy settling is that a baby will often push themselves up, or, if crawling, will crawl up to the top of the cot, so you have to gently slide them back down to the middle of the bed and repeat the tapping (see Settling checklist, page 77).

Sometimes when I manage to calm a baby on their tummy, I notice that they do not really like it or look uncomfortable and so once they are almost

*Patience, confidence and repetition are
the most important things to remember.
Putting new practices or routines into
place takes roughly 3–5 days.*

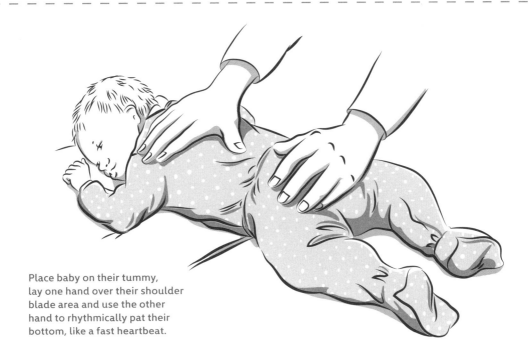

Place baby on their tummy,
lay one hand over their shoulder
blade area and use the other
hand to rhythmically pat their
bottom, like a fast heartbeat.

asleep I will turn them onto their side to finally settle them to sleep and then possibly back onto their back.

Patience, confidence and repetition are the most important things to remember. Putting new practices or routines into place takes roughly 3–5 days. Your first day may not be too hard and in fact some babies will respond straight away and settle on their own or with ease after 2–3 days, but most older babies often take up to a week to really trust what you are doing and feel your confidence.

Put aside some time to implement the change. There is no point starting a method like this if you know you are going to be out during their day sleeps or you are going away or have visitors coming. Having a calm environment helps you and your baby.

Tummy settling

Once a baby is able to move about the cot the settling action is different from when they were younger, but the concept is exactly the same.

The difference is that once they are able to understand words, you use words and action rather than just action (and a little 'shhh-ing'). Alongside the tummy-settling technique, I would use my 'supervised settling' technique or 'pick up and put down' technique (see page 97).

SETTLING CHECKLIST

- When you hear your baby start to cry (not complain or grizzle), start your timing. Leave them for 3–5 minutes if they are not over-tired or 1–2 minutes if they were already tired when you put them down.
- Walk into the room and loudly make the 'shhh' sounds. The 'shhh' is to help calm and should be louder than their cry.
- Quickly and confidently, turn them onto their tummy (if you are too slow and gentle they will sense your fear of doing something new).
- Continuing with the 'shhh' sound, place your hand with a gentle but confident pressure over their shoulder blades with your fingers gently over their upper arm (preventing them from turning back towards you, and to give them comfort). With your other hand tap their bottom quickly in a heartbeat rhythm. Your tap is now more of a pat, unlike the newborn tap, which might not create enough movement or comfort at this stage.
- I find that using the inside of my wrist or the palm of my hand for tapping rather than my fingers is better when my hand is getting tired.
- As they calm, you make the tapping softer and slower and make your 'shhh' sound quieter and slower, eventually stopping.
- Increase and decrease the speed and change the type of the tap/shunt depending on their mood and reaction to your settling. If your baby starts to complain again, increase your speed, slowing as they calm.
- If they are trying to crawl up the cot or attempting to twist and turn over, let them move. Once they have got to the top of the cot or have turned over, roll or slide them back into the middle of the cot and start the tapping again. I try about three times before I leave the room.
- If they are resisting your attempt to settle, leave the room, take a deep breath and let them grizzle or cry for 3–5 minutes (or just 1–2 minutes if they are very upset) and then enter and repeat. Or, if you are using the 'pick up and put down' method, pick them up until they are calm and then place back into bed.
- I would repeat this up to three times before picking them up and standing by the cot, cuddling them firmly (saying 'shhh' or 'calm down' loudly) and bouncing or rocking them to calm. This should only take a minute or so. As soon as they are calm place them back into bed. You can at any time choose to pick them up instead of leaving the room; always try, however, to put them back into bed to 'finish' off the settling.

It may take three or four attempts to finally settle your baby when you are first learning how to settle them to sleep in a bed. Often babies stir about 5 minutes after falling asleep as they slip into their deep sleep. So when your baby is calm and asleep, just wait patiently with one hand very faintly sitting on their bottom, ready to start a little jiggle if they stir at the 5-minute mark. I find that babies often do a little 'sigh' or twitch just as they go into their deep sleep.

Night waking

If your baby is frequently waking in the night, not because they are hungry just out of habit, I suggest you think firstly about what is happening in the day.

Look at their routine. If they are still having three good sleeps a day, they may be ready to move to my transition routine (two good sleeps and one smaller sleep; see Suggested routine: Stage 3 on page 158), which ensures they are tired enough to sleep for longer periods at night.

Night waking can also occur because your baby is hungry and may almost be ready for solid food. They may not be interested in solids initially so you have to be patient with the waking until they are ready or you may need to look at offering an extra feed during the day, either an extra breastfeed or an expressed milk top-up bottle. If using formula I would suggest you try offering a bottle after their afternoon sleep and then again before and after their bath – this will replicate a 'cluster' feed.

A dream feed at this age can sometimes cause babies to wake more often if they no longer need it. (See Stage 3 Daily Routine on page 158.)

Once you have changed your routine and you know that they are not hungry, then look at settling them instead of feeding them when they wake. I would use my 'supervised settling' technique (see page 97); however, for the first two nights I will often respond quickly rather than leaving them to complain – this might mean you can help them back to sleep before they have had a chance to wake up too much. If they are not responding, however, carry on with my 'supervised settling' recommendations.

Below is a typical night-waking scenario and how I would deal with it.
You put your baby to bed at 7pm and give them a dream feed at 10pm but they are waking again at 1am, 3am and 5am.
I like to have goals rather than rules. When your baby wakes before 1–2am, I would try to resettle them for up to 30–45 minutes without feeding. If you are successful, feed them when they next wake, then again in the morning. If you are not successful, feed them now; when they next wake (if before 5am) try to resettle them for up to 30–45 minutes without

feeding. Over the period of 3–5 days your baby will start to learn to self-settle and sleep through those occasions when previously they would have woken for a 'quick fix' feed.

When you have successfully reduced the number of times they wake, you should move your 'goal' time from 1–2am to 3–4am. You may, however, like to stay with this first stage of improvement for a few days to catch up on sleep and have a break from settling and also your baby may start to improve on their own.

I would do this for three days and if they are still waking I would look at their day feeding and sleeping routine again.

NOTE: When a baby wakes less in the night they might not need quite as much sleep during the day as they did before. Sleep does breed sleep and for the first three days of sleeping more at night they should sleep well in the day but soon they will have caught up on sleep and their awake time might need to increase by 10–15 minutes.

Weaning off being swaddled

Most babies don't need to be swaddled by three months of age but others may need it until they are 4–6 months. Below are some signs that your baby might be ready to stop being swaddled to sleep:

• They are now rolling from back to tummy during play. If your baby rolls in their bed while swaddled they will be unable to push themselves up off the mattress, which is unsafe.
• They are 'breaking out' of their swaddle but can stay asleep.
• They are struggling to self-settle when put down because they are frustrated they cannot get their arms or hands out.
• You think they are showing signs of wanting to suck their hand or thumb, or if using a dummy they may even try to put it back in on their own.
• They are no longer startling when being put down on the ground, into the bath or when they are surprised by noise.

Instead of stopping 'cold turkey', as such, I suggest you try half-swaddling. To do this you follow the instructions on page 76, but leave one arm out (their bottom arm if turning onto their side to settle), wrapping the top arm away, as this is the arm that can move around freely and will keep them awake.

Try this for one or all of their day sleeps and then, once they are okay with it, try it at night-time, too. Babies who sleep well at night may not respond as well to half-swaddling in the day, so it may be better to try it with them first at night when there is little stimulation and noise. They may still require a little settling for the first 1–3 days.

A lot of people ask me if and when they should move their baby into a sleeping bag. I normally always recommend it, particularly in the winter months when they may kick off their covers and wake cold. Babies learn to relate being put into their sleeping bag (wherever they may be) with their sleep time and it becomes familiar and comforting.

Introducing a bottle

There is no right time to wean a baby but I have put this information in the 4–6 month age group as that is when I find most people are starting to ask me questions on how to go about it. The longer you breastfeed, the better it is for your baby, but whatever works for you is what is most important.

The process of weaning or introducing a bottle can be very challenging when starting at a later age. You are very lucky if your baby takes the bottle straight away! Whether you are trying to add in one bottle a day or planning to start weaning your baby from the breast completely, I suggest you do so in a gradual manner as the older baby will reject your attempts if you push them too much and a gradual process also helps your breast milk supply to slowly reduce, lessening the possibility of having engorged breasts or mastitis.

How to start weaning

In the past it was recommended that if a baby was rejecting the bottle the mother should go away for a weekend and a grandparent or the father should offer the baby the bottle over that time. I, however, have found that in most situations the mother is the best person to offer the bottle, as long as it is done correctly, because they have been their main caregiver while feeding and their main source of comfort.

Instead of starting straight on formula I would always suggest to start on a little expressed breast milk. This way you will know whether your baby is unhappy with the teat rather than wondering whether it could be the taste.

Start by expressing just a tiny amount (20–30 ml) for them to try, increasing how much you offer them as they become more accepting of it. If you do not enjoy or have no luck with expressing, then just make up the minimum amount of formula, usually 50 ml.

I like to start by using a bottle that has what I call an 'old-fashioned teat'; a straight up and down, narrow neck teat, not an orthodontic or 'nipple look-alike' teat. The reason for this is that older babies can push a shaped teat around or out of their mouth because of its flexibility. I like the teats that come with the Green to Grow bottles or rubber teats, which have a better texture in the baby's mouth.

If you are demand feeding your baby small amounts frequently, you will find that you are best to try to push out the time between their last breastfeed and first bottle feed so they are hungry enough to try. You do not want to make them unhappy but just a little more hungry than they may be used to.

* Position

Hold your baby in the cradle position to begin with, distracting them with a little rocking motion from side to side if necessary. (See illustration on page 46.) If you find that they arch their back in this position then I would suggest you offer the bottle when they are sitting in a baby chair or propped up on a pillow as they will then not be frustrated by being so close to your breast and it will be seen as a different food source, not a replacement.

* Time of day

If you still have the dream feed in place this may be a good time to give your baby their first bottle feed as they will be very sleepy; usually a baby rejects the bottle because they are wide awake and aware. However, if you have no success at this time or are not giving a dream feed, I would suggest the following.

First offer your baby the bottle for their early afternoon feed. If you are feeding on routine it would be the 2pm feed. Offer the bottle to your baby as soon as they wake and while they are still sleepy. If they reject this after you have been trying for about 5–10 minutes I would offer a small breastfeed and then try the bottle again 30–40 minutes later. Let them have little sips and then leave it for a bit before offering again (make sure you use the milk roughly within an hour of being heated). If your baby still is not interested then I would offer the breast again before their next sleep.

Each day I would offer the bottle at the same time of day, just little bits and often, until your baby is happy to take the bottle and drinks enough that you can stop offering the breast.

Some women will need to express and discard their milk during the weaning process. Try to slowly reduce the amount you are expressing until you feel comfortable enough to stop altogether. For example, express for 8 minutes on days 1 and 2, then just 5 minutes on days 3 and 4, and so on. Women who have a lower milk supply at this time of day may not need to express and should be okay with missing this feed but should still keep an eye on their breasts over this time of weaning to ensure you don't get blocked milk ducts from the change in feeding patterns.

When your baby is happy to take on the bottle once a day you can start weaning them properly. Opposite is an example of how to wean over a 3-week period. It can be achieved more quickly if necessary.

My suggestion for weaning over a 3-week period

Week 1	
6–7am	Breastfeed
10am	Breastfeed
2pm	Introduce first bottle feed (expressing if needed)
6pm	Breastfeed

Week 2	
6–7am	Breastfeed
10am	Introduce second bottle feed (expressing if needed)
2pm	Bottle feed (expressing if needed)
6pm	Breastfeed

Week 3	
6–7am	Introduce third or fourth bottle feed (expressing if needed)
10am	Bottle feed (expressing if needed)
2pm	Bottle feed (expressing if needed)
6pm*	Introduce third bottle feed (expressing if needed)

* Some mothers find that the 6pm feed can be split to begin with, offering breast before the bath and then a bottle top-up afterwards before bed, or vice versa.

IMPORTANT

If you feel a lump or see any redness on the skin of your breast and/or if you feel unwell, seek help from your doctor as it may be a breast infection or mastitis. Have a hot shower and massage your breast in downward strokes. Express enough to ease the lump. Drink plenty of water and get sufficient rest.

Introducing solid food

When to start your baby on solid food is a much-debated topic. While most health professionals suggest that your baby will be ready for solid food at six months of age, I rather think that advice is too much 'one style fits all' and, in my opinion, it depends on the weight of your baby and their interest in watching you eat.

What we know is that babies post 6 months of age need extra iron and nutrients from solid food and that a slow introduction of solid meals from roughly this age is advised. Some babies, however, will be indicating at an earlier age through their body language and baby talk that they are very interested in what you are putting in your mouth.

You might suspect that your baby is ready for solids if they were sleeping well at night or in the day and all of sudden have started waking and wanting more milk, but are not satisfied by what you are offering them.

Once you have your baby on solid food I strongly recommend that you think carefully about the types of food you offer them. I have become incredibly passionate about what food we feed our babies and children from seeing its effects on health. I, personally, believe that certain foods are linked with behaviour, illness and the daily well-being of us all and from experience have seen how the right foods can help, if not heal, illnesses or conditions.

You have the foundation of your child's future diet in your hands: the flavours and tastes, variety and quality of food that you introduce now will have an effect in the future.

If you are interested in learning more about healthy food for your baby, I recommend *The Complete Baby and Toddler Meal Planner* (great for recipes) or *Feeding Your Baby and Toddler* by Annabel Karmel, *Organic Baby and Toddler Cookbook* by Lizzie Vann and *Whole Food for Children* by Jude Blereau. A useful website is www.wholesomebabyfood.momtastic.com

When to start and which foods

I recommend you slowly start introducing solids to your baby's diet at any stage from 4–6 months; most babies are between 5 and 6 months of age. If you have any concerns, talk with a health professional or your doctor. If you are starting solids just before 6 months of age then I normally suggest you start your baby on cooked fruit or vegetables (it may be just for 1–2 weeks) to allow your baby's digestive system to adjust to this new food source and help prevent any constipation.

In my experience, babies who at this older age are still having very frequent bowel motions (at least 3–4 times a day) are okay to start on baby rice or millet cereal as their first solid food as it appears their active digestive system can cope with being slowed down a little!

Once your baby's bowel motions have adapted, and by this I mean they are not too firm and they occur daily or every other day, then you can add in iron-fortified foods. It is very important that they get this iron from food like baby rice or millet cereal, but I like to transition a baby into it rather than 'shock' the digestive system!

Be wary of offering your baby too many fruit meals over vegetable meals. Babies are naturally attracted to sweet flavours (like breast milk) and soon cotton on to loving sweet flavours only!

Cook (steam or stew) the majority of your baby's fruit and vegetable meals until they are closer to 8 or 9 months of age. A baby's digestive system is sensitive during these initial months and cooked food is easier to digest than raw. Some babies respond well to a little expressed breast milk or formula added to their baby rice or millet cereal, rather than just using water.

Unlike a lot of advice, I also try to stay away from too much gluten, offering wheat-free bread toast fingers and using millet or brown rice cereals rather than wheat bread or wheat cereals. I believe this may help prevent future intolerances or sensitivities to certain foods.

* My first foods list

Fruit: (4–6 months) pear, melon, peach, avocado, mango or nectarine; (over 6 months) gold kiwifruit (I like to try to offer fruit that is in season so it is well ripened)

Vegetables: (4–6 months) pumpkin/squash, courgette (zucchini) and green beans; (6 months) golden kumara

Other: (6 months) ground baby rice, millet, sago

It is worthwhile noting that banana can be offered this early but it is one food that I have found some babies and children can have an intolerance to and so I tend to only offer it later, post 8 months of age. I first noticed this when working for a naturopath many years ago. When banana was removed from a breastfeeding mother's diet, the snuffly nose her newborn had went away. The other symptom you may notice is a wheezy and congested-sounding chest. If you notice any of these signs, I would seek advice from a doctor or naturopath.

* How to start

Weeks 1–2:
Offer 3–4 teaspoons just once a day. If your baby looks as if they would like more, increase the quantity slightly as long as they have had their milk feed beforehand.

Weeks 2–3:
Offer a second meal to their day, again just offering small amounts. 1–2 tablespoons would be plenty.

Weeks 3–4:
Add in a third meal to your baby's daily routine as long as they are eager to eat. Some babies don't need a third meal for another week or two.

Once they are on three meals a day you can start to be a little more inventive with what you offer, rather than keeping to the same flavours all the time.

COOKING TIPS!

• Steam or stew most fruit and vegetables in the first 2–3 months on solid food; this is vital for keeping the nutrients and goodness in the food source and is more digestible than raw food.

• Keep any vegetable juice from your meals to use as stock. This is the best way to pour back into food any lost nutrients and also great for thinning any foods when they have got too thick with the heating process. I freeze it in ice-cube trays or keep it fresh in a glass jar in the fridge.

• Don't use a microwave (unless you have to). Babies and children need every single vitamin possible to fight off colds and bugs that they come across, especially if attending a nursery school or playgroup.

• Roast garlic in the oven (in the skin) and squeeze out the soft cloves, adding to vegetables or savoury meals once your baby is post 1 year of age. Roasting the garlic takes away the strong flavour. I suggest you use one garlic clove per 3–4 cups of food. This is a brilliant way of keeping the bugs at bay in the winter.

• Freeze prepared food in ice-cube trays and then when frozen empty into labelled zip-lock bags or BPA-free plastic tubs.

• Offer water from a (sipper) cup with each meal (cooled boiled water to start with) or offer little sips from a cup.

Developmental play: 4–6 months

The active baby stage has begun. Given the opportunity your baby will be moving around quite a bit on the floor, their play mat or in bed; some are rolling from back to tummy but not quite back again, some are pushing themselves up on their arms and are ready to take on this interesting environment. The inquisitive baby will be holding toys in their hands and putting them in their mouth as they learn not only about the texture and sound of their toys but the taste of them, too.

Ideas to add to activity time

* Reaching

Choose a few toys or objects of interest and place near your baby while they are sitting or having tummy time. Watch them accidentally push the toys away in their attempt to pick up or touch the object and then reach for it again. This is great for developing their hand–eye coordination. Try not to place too many toys around your baby, just a few at a time. If you notice there is a particular toy or object your baby likes over a few days, it is nice to include that toy in your selected few as this will encourage determination on your baby's part to reach for that favourite object.

* Shadow play

It is wonderful to watch babies who are lying or sitting and creating a shadow. By doing simple activities like this you are stimulating the cognitive part of their development. Move your hand or your body slowly to create a moving shadow for your baby to watch!

* Peek-a-boo

This is such a simple but fun game to start teaching your baby. I like to use a soft piece of material like a muslin wrap and drape it briefly over them, lifting it up into the air as soon as it touches their face so it doesn't frighten them. If your baby is a little weary of this game, you can cover yourself instead. Repeating a game like this several times slowly will give a baby the chance to think about what is happening and how they will respond.

* Texture time

This was one of my all-time favourite activities when I was working in a nursery school/daycare because the reaction on the babies' faces was so interesting!

Touch your baby's feet on the grass or let them sit on the grass and touch it with their hands. Simply feeling grass is a new sensation for them. (Always watch out for plants or small objects in the grass that may not be safe for your baby.)

Fill a big basket, tub or box with scrunched-up paper or leaves and sit your baby inside – this will open their minds to different textures. (When using paper or leaves for filling a basket use soft and non-toxic materials.)

I notice that some of my clients now don't give their babies the opportunity to feel natural textures in the environment, fearing they will get dirty or that they may put something in their mouths that is not safe. Experiencing the outside world is wonderful for a number of their developmental skills, just make sure you are there watching and monitoring the activity.

CHAPTER 6

7–9 months

You will now be enjoying an active and mobile baby. Watch your baby carefully but allow them time to learn and discover. Enjoy more freedom to get out and about as your baby's ability to cope with activity improves – I call this reduction in juggling sleep times the 'home straight'!

Basic needs: 7–9 months

- Now your baby is more mobile it is time to secure the house so they have a safe environment. Babies move very quickly and can reach the other end of the house in no time. Crawling or pulling themselves up onto furniture might have started and with this some falls and tears will occur.

- Most babies at seven months go through a period that some refer to as 'separation anxiety'. They are more aware of where you are and need reassurance that you are not too far away from them. They are just starting to learn at this stage 'object constancy': the knowledge that things and people are constant and if you go away you will come back.

- Babies now do not need as much sleep in the day as they did previously. Two sleeps a day is usually enough if you want them to settle and sleep well at night.

- Your baby will be having three meals a day and their milk intake is starting to become equal to their solid food intake. By one year they will be having solid food as their main food source so this period of time is their transition into that next phase.

- Your baby can now explore more finger foods in their diet. If using the baby-led weaning method (letting a baby feed themselves, with little or no spoon-fed food) you should be mindful that if they are too tired they will often not eat enough and might need more feeding during the night. I like to offer both finger foods and mashed foods fed with a spoon to babies at this age.

Common questions: 7–9 months

Why won't my baby let me feed her with a spoon? Why does she turn his head away when I try to offer her food?

If your baby is eating enough food to be happy and is sleeping well then you have nothing to worry about; there is plenty of time for them to get used to being spoon fed. Don't offer food when your baby is too tired as they will be less receptive.

Make sure the 'baby' food or mashed food tastes nice and you would eat it! Often I see mums still using only jar food, which can be bland. Texture is also important and your baby may not like lumps in their food. It is okay if your baby will only have mashed food when it is very smooth, just be happy that they are eating! Also this is common when a baby is teething, as their gums are sensitive.

Babies love flavours at this age and can eat a lot of what you eat as long as it is not seasoned too much and there are no lumps they can choke on.

If you find that most of the food goes on the floor and you are worried about how much they are actually eating, try distracting them by singing or let them hold something, like a spoon or something from your kitchen drawer that is safe, then when they take it to their mouth you put the spoon in. (Be aware that using distraction may become a hard habit to break.) If you find that things are not improving, try offering smaller meals 4–5 times a day.

You should never force your baby to eat, however, as this will only put them off even more.

Should I be offering my baby water during the day?

Yes, this is important now that your baby is having solid food. I offer them water during or after a meal and now and then during their playtime.

If your baby doesn't like to use a sipper cup, try an adult cup. Often babies will take it because it is something that you use and they do not have to suck. Just make sure it is not glass, as some babies will bite on it if teething. Offer small sips controlled by you to begin with.

What can I do to help my baby when she is teething?

This is a challenging time as your baby's sleep, eating habits and happiness may change. There are some natural remedies that I suggest you use: teething drops from a naturopath, teething granules or a teething powder. Talk with a naturopath or a health professional about these products. (NOTE: *Some of these products have lactose in them, so if your baby is lactose intolerant you may need to use one that doesn't.*)

I like to use teething necklaces (amber bead necklaces); however, there are some who disagree with this product's use. Once again, talk with health professionals you respect if you have concerns.

I also like to raise the head of their cot slightly by placing books under the legs at the head or a folded towel under the mattress. This helps to reduce the throbbing in their gum area. Make sure you don't raise the head too high or they might roll to the bottom of the bed!

How do I help my baby who seems constipated during the day (but has a bowel motion in the middle of the night)?

This can be related to what you are feeding them. Look at the fibre they have from vegetables, fruits and cereals as well as their water intake in the day. I like to offer the fibrous foods at breakfast and lunch and less at dinnertime until you have broken the night habit! I would suggest, however, that you talk with a health professional about this as there may be other reasons this is occurring.

Why is my baby 'clingy' to me? She does not even like being left with her father or grandmother whom she sees regularly.

This is commonly known as 'separation anxiety'. A nicer description is that your baby is more aware of where you are and what you are doing and needs to know, through repetition and guidance, that you are always going to come back.

When you are about to leave the room, let them know where you are going, for example, 'Mummy is just going to the loo'. In the beginning only leave for a brief moment so they learn that it is just for a short period and you'll soon be back.

Running back to them as soon as you hear them complain is okay but this may prolong the length of time they go through this stage of their development. Let your partner and others know that your baby is not rejecting them, it is just a normal part of your baby's development. They may need to let your baby get used to them before they are happy to be held or cuddled or left in their company.

Using distraction is the key. Tell your partner or caregiver what your baby likes, or suggest a walk in the garden or buggy, a noisy favourite toy or a dummy (if using).

While saying goodbye is important (more so at their next stage of development – 10 months plus), if you find that your baby gets more upset when watching you leave, try to prevent this by kissing them goodbye and then leaving when your baby is distracted and/or happy.

When I ran a daycare/preschool, we often had to use distraction when new babies or children started with us. Musical toys always worked well, as did a walk outside.

Trusting the person you are leaving your baby with is important, as your baby will sense your confidence in the situation.

Why won't my baby settle in the evening when we are aiming for a 7pm bedtime?
This is commonly because they are having too much sleep in the day so you need to look at how late your baby is going to sleep in the afternoon and for how long. You may have to be flexible with their bedtime when they are transitioning from three to two sleeps a day. The days they need to have a longer afternoon sleep, or if they have to go back to three sleeps a day due to having shorter sleeps in the day, you may need to make bedtime a little later (7.30–8pm).

You may have offered them dinner a little too late in the day and they were too tired to eat well. I like to try to offer dinner at this age around 5–5.30pm; even as early as 4.30–5pm.

When I try to settle my baby he sits up in the cot. What can I do to stop him moving?
The freedom of movement is wonderful for them and you do need to be patient with this. I like to teach them how to deal with this new freedom by letting them move around or even stand up, but if it prevents them settling to sleep then I use my settling technique to show them what is expected of them, i.e, it is sleep time not playtime!

Using a baby sleeping bag is a good idea now as it means they can fall asleep without you worrying if they are under their covers or not.

I personally would not prevent them from being able to move by using any product that 'fixes' a baby in one position as movement is just part of their natural development. When they are teething they need to be able to move to find comfort. It might mean more work for you, showing them how to settle again, but it is your role as their parent, in my opinion, to help teach them at each stage of their development.

Is it okay for my baby to sleep on her tummy now? When I go in to check on her I always find her on her tummy.
As long as your baby can move freely and can push themselves up on their hands or is crawling, I believe it is safe for them to sleep on their tummy. If, however, you have any concerns, talk with your doctor.

Keep the cot free of anything your baby may get tangled or stuck in or that could come apart, e.g., soft toys that have buttons or eyes that could come off if sucked.

My baby bangs her head on the cot when she is moving about. Can I use a cot bumper to prevent her hurting herself?

When some babies get upset or if they are uncomfortable with teething they bang their heads as a means of expressing their frustration. It is normally just a short phase of their development. Using a cot bumper that is fixed firmly to a cot is okay but I would not use any that your baby has the ability to get stuck under. Most cot bumpers I see gape too much and it would be possible for a baby to get their head underneath. The one that I like to use is called an 'Air Wrap' and fits very firmly to a cot.

If the head banging concerns you, talk with your doctor or health professional.

Settling your baby: 7–9 months

I see a lot of families with babies of this age; they are going through their transition from being a newborn to a baby and in this time a lot happens in their world.

When parents contact me with questions about why their baby is not settling or sleeping well at night I firstly ask how often their baby is sleeping during the day and for how long.

At 6–7 months of age most babies, particularly those in a routine, will be ready for two sleeps a day for the majority of the week but, due to disrupted sleep at night or shorter sleeps during the day, they may need a catch-up day or two when they will have three or four sleeps.

Whether you want a routine in place or not, if you would like your baby to know how to sleep better at night or during the day, you need to think about how the daily pattern is working. It is like being in 'groundhog day' if you do not change what is happening in the day, i.e., if your baby wakes a lot in the night they will need more sleep during the day, but the more sleep they have during the day, the less they need at night.

You have to take little steps, changing their daytime sleeping patterns gradually, extending the time you keep your baby up first thing in the morning by 10–15 minutes. I commonly see the following pattern:

• Baby wakes in the night more than once or is hard to settle to sleep in the evening but sleeps all night.
• Baby wakes between 6 and 7am and shows tired signs 1½–2 hours later, going to bed at 8–9am.
• Because baby is not quite tired enough they only sleep for one sleep cycle, roughly 30–45 minutes.

- Baby wakes tired but happy enough but can only stay awake for another 1½–2 hours.
- Baby then sleeps another short sleep of roughly 45 minutes.
- Baby wakes around 4–4.30pm.
- Baby is hard to settle in the evening or settles but wakes again or several times in the night.

To change this pattern, you need to increase their awake time by distracting them (walk in the garden or nappy-free time) when they show you a tired sign. In conjunction with this, you may need to use a settling technique to help them get to sleep or go back to sleep after waking from one sleep cycle.

Lack of sleep can have quite an influence on your baby's ability to cope with meal times. They will eat less as their ability to concentrate and their appetite are affected. If they are teething, their discomfort can be heightened due to their tiredness.

As I have mentioned before, some parents are happy when a baby of this age is waking at night or having short naps during the day. I recommend that if you are not happy with this current routine, you try using my 'supervised settling' technique (see page 97) to help them to move to a two-sleep-a-day routine. (See also pages 116–121 for guidance on how to settle an older baby.)

Developmental play: 7–9 months

Sitting and reaching has begun. Babies may be on the move, either by commando rolling or crawling, and are keen to discover this new world that is now in their reach!

This new ability to move will mean you have to be more aware of where you have things placed in the house. It's time to assess the safety of your house as babies can move quickly and quietly when they focus on something of interest.

A baby who isn't showing much interest in movement may be a visual baby who is more interested in objects within their reach, the movements of others, particularly their main caregiver, and sounds.

Ideas to add to activity time

* Posting box

Babies love to open and shut and look inside things now they have found more freedom to explore. Creating a posting box helps them to learn how objects fit inside things and how to problem-solve or discover where things have gone.

I use either an old tissue box, making the hole big enough for a baby's hand to post a small object in and out, or an old baby formula tin with a hole cut in the plastic lid. Remember to check for any sharp edges.

Show them how to do this activity and keep it interesting as time goes on by offering different-sized objects rather than just the small items that you know will fit.

* Come and find me

This is such a fun game to play when your baby is moving around your house, and is particularly good if they are showing signs of being a little worried when you move away from them. To show your baby how to play this game start by crawling in the direction they are moving in and then hide behind something that is near them (e.g. sofa) and peek out and say 'Come and find me' or 'Where is Daddy?', etc.

* Family faces

Fill a scrapbook or an album with photographs of the important people in your family life. This is great to do when you have family who live far away. Don't forget to include photos of the family pet(s)!

I like to make the pictures quite large so the people's faces are big enough for a baby to see. If you are filling a scrapbook, use cover seal or laminate the photos so your baby can touch it without damaging it.

* Clapping and tapping

Music and movement really starts to become fun at this age with your baby. If you have been singing songs from an early age with your baby by now they will be recognising tunes and you can start teaching them movement and rhythm.

Choose songs that are slow and are action songs like:

My hands are clapping, clapping, clapping,
My hands are clapping, clapping, clapping,
My hands are clapping, just like this.

Change the words to create new verses: my eyes are blinking; my fingers are wriggling; and so on.

Fill a scrapbook or an album with photographs of the important people in your family life. Use cover seal or laminate the photos so your baby can touch it without damaging it.

CHAPTER 7

10–12 months

Your baby is now becoming a little person, almost a toddler, and with this comes a new independence and ability to communicate.

Basic needs: 10–12 months

- Talk to your baby and tell them what is happening ('It's dinnertime. Come and sit in your highchair. Good girl', or 'Let's go and get dressed now'.) This will encourage their chatter and development of words. You may have started doing this at an earlier age, which is wonderful, but from now it is important as this will help a baby to express any emotion or discomfort in the future.

- Some babies may be clearly showing you their preferences at this age, like when you ask them to stay still while having their nappy changed or hop into a buggy when leaving the playground! They may like you to hold their hand and walk beside you as part of their play.

- They are now almost ready to drop down to three milk feeds a day, however, if they are happily eating solid food while still feeding on demand or are still having four milk feeds on a routine, that is okay. I would only drop down to three if they are preferring milk to solid food.

- Some babies may sleep a little less during the day until they start walking, which will tire them to begin with. Two sleeps a day is what is most common but some active babies might drop down to one sleep a day, 2–3 days a week, depending on what you are doing during the day.

- Your baby understands the word 'no' and when you use it too often you may find you are giving more attention to the behaviour that you do not like, instead of praising and giving attention when they are playing quietly and doing what you see as okay.

Common questions: 10–12 months

By this stage of your baby's development you will both know each other well and you may not have as many questions as previously. Remember to look back through the earlier ages and stages if you're struggling with a problem I have not listed below.

My baby has stopped going to sleep in the afternoon and has only just turned one. Isn't this too early?

This is okay for some babies; it all depends on how happy they are in the evening, their ability to eat a meal in the evening and how early they end up in bed (which can affect the time they wake in the morning).

Look at how long you are letting them sleep in the morning. If they sleep for 2 hours but then will not sleep in the afternoon and they are shattered by 5pm, I would suggest you wake your baby after an hour in the morning so they will have a nap, either in bed or in a buggy/car in the afternoon to see them through to dinnertime and to help keep a later bedtime.

Another option is to push out the time in the morning that you put them down to sleep so they are sleeping in the late morning/midday rather than around 10–11am. You will need to start by giving a bigger morning tea and then lunch when they wake. As they adjust to one sleep at 12pm(ish) you can offer lunch before their sleep at 11–11.30am, and go back to a smaller morning tea.

There will be a transition phase, just like when they move from three sleeps to two (see Stage 3 and 4 Daily Routines on pages 158 and 161) where they may cope with one sleep a day for 2–3 days a week but then will go back to having two sleeps for the rest of the week.

Changing my baby's nappy has become a real battle. How can I stop her twisting and rolling away?

Oh, this is the joy of a baby who likes their independence! While I understand it is incredibly frustrating for you, I would suggest that you try not to give the behaviour too much attention. If you focus on the negative, most babies will respond by increasing the behaviour as they see it as a game.

I like to use distraction. Have a few 'tools' on hand for your baby to hold. Objects that they do not normally play with are good, like a bracelet, necklace or a set of keys.

While distraction is my first choice in most cases, it is okay, in my opinion, to start setting boundaries by using firm words, for example, 'Daddy would like you to stay still, please. Good girl.' When your baby does lie still, even if for just a moment, distract them and then praise them for listening. 'Look at what I've got [passing them something], good girl.'

If this is not working, think about when you are changing their nappy. Is it during their playtime or while they are immersed in an activity? Do you really need to change their nappy right at that moment? Sometimes, yes, you will, and sometimes you could actually wait a while!

I am still breastfeeding but am thinking of stopping soon. I have tried to offer my baby a bottle but she just pushes it away. What shall I do? There is no real need for a baby to go onto a bottle at this age; using a sipper cup is okay. However, if you do use a cup it is important to maintain the same snuggle time that they had while on the breast. There are not many opportunities for a baby of this age to lie still and cuddle!

If you want to introduce a bottle, do it in stages throughout the week before you give up feeding or when they are on the sipper cup. Try giving them a bottle a couple of times a day while they are quietly playing or sitting on your lap having a story. (See Introducing a bottle on page 121.)

Settling your baby: 10–12 months

Your baby is almost a toddler now. With this new phase comes more understanding and possibly more resistance to being settled to sleep.

As with a baby from 6 months, I will settle a baby of this age on their tummy but now introduce a few words, as their understanding of instructions is beginning to develop and they are not stimulated by voices as much as when they were a baby. I do, however, still use the 'shhh' sound to comfort them as it is familiar.

I have used this technique many times with babies who were settled in their sleep but have regressed because of illness or a change of some sort to their lives. I also use it with babies who are learning to settle on their own (without being fed to sleep or co-sleeping with a parent). The use of words alongside my settling technique will help a baby who is a little upset or annoyed with this change to their settling.

Your baby is almost a toddler now. With this new phase comes more understanding and possibly more resistance to being settled to sleep.

SETTLING CHECKLIST

- Do not take too long moving your baby to their own room. Once you have read their stories (as many as you like out of the bedroom, but limit it to two books in the bedroom), give them a cuddle and put them into bed. Once you have finished the stories they should be in bed within 2 minutes! I have found that if you take too long they start to pick up on your anxiety or fear and hope this drawn-out calming process will go on forever.
- As you place them into bed, give them a kiss and say you love them then leave the room.
- If your baby doesn't settle I would start 'supervised settling', using the 'in and out of the room' technique (see page 97).
- First, let them complain for 3–5 minutes if they are crying consistently or 10–15 minutes if it's inconsistent. The first time you enter the room say words like, 'Shhh, lie down, sleep time now, good girl, shhh'. As you are saying these, move confidently to their cot and lie them down.
- If they respond and lie down (with or without your help) I would tap/pat their bottom quickly in the heartbeat rhythm, slowing the speed down in accordance with their behaviour until they are asleep. On day 2 and 3 I would continue settling them until they are calm.
- If they are not responding to your settling, leave the room and as you are leaving say 'Shhh. Sleep time. Mummy will come back'. Walk out quickly, don't linger.
- The second time you leave them to complain, leave for 2–3 minutes if they are consistently crying or 8–10 minutes if it's inconsistent.
- Enter the room and repeat what you did before, this time staying in the room for up to 5 minutes on day 1 and then as per the Settling checklist on page 118 for the remaining days. Try lying them down three times (if they are wriggling or standing back up) before leaving the room again. It should not be a battle, you just need patience to show them what you are trying to do, and that you are the parent!
- The third time you leave them to complain only leave for 1–2 minutes or 30 seconds if very distressed.

Repeat all of this until your baby is asleep, but if you are having no success after 4–5 attempts and they are very distressed, pick them up, giving them a cuddle very briefly, and then put them down, going straight to settling (patting) and try to settle until asleep.

If their understanding is good then you can use more words, for example, 'If you stop crying Mummy will come into the room, okay? Have you stopped crying? Good girl.' Or, 'Mummy will just go and wash the dishes (or go to the toilet, etc.) and I will come and see you in five minutes. Good girl.' And so on.

It is all about distraction, reassurance and repetition. If you only try once or twice your baby will know to resist for longer as they know that you will pick them up and go back to the method of settling you were trying to stop.

Developmental play: 10–12 months

Almost one year on your baby is a little person. Some will be walking but most are just thinking about it! All babies at this age are very inquisitive. Not only do they have a new-found freedom of movement but they also have found their voice and are trying out many sounds, even words like 'Dada' and 'Mama'. They become little observers, mimicking and retaining words and actions of your own or others around them.

Active babies may have a few knocks while the 'observers' may be spared them. It's all about being a big baby now, discovering and doing things on their own often to get your attention or a reaction, like throwing food on the floor!

They have the ability to understand commands or requests like 'Let's change your nappy', 'Please lie down. Good girl' or 'Can Mummy have a kiss?' and simple questions like 'Where is . . . ?'

It is all about distraction, reassurance and repetition. If you only try once or twice your baby will know to resist for longer.

Ideas to add to activity time

* Where is my nose?

When your baby is in a quiet moment of the day or when you have time together lying in bed (morning snuggles), start teaching your baby about their body parts by asking them to point to your nose, etc. and then in return you can ask them, 'Where is your nose?'

* Stacking

Babies now have the ability to stack one or two blocks or cups, learning about balance. Stacking cups are great as they are different colours and different sizes so you can talk about colours as you are playing. They will also learn about crashing and falling as their blocks or cups fall, particularly if you have built a tower that is tall and tempting and they reach to touch the wonderful sight!

* Finger painting

Most parents avoid any activity that involves paint, but if you let your baby try finger painting you will quickly see just how much they love it. Using non-toxic paint and old clothes or an apron is essential.

If they try to put the paint in their mouth, instead of saying 'no' just direct their fingers with your hand onto the paper and show them what happens and how it feels when they slide their fingers over the paper.

You can use an easel or simply get some cheap newsprint or recycled paper and tape it down on top of a small table. The paper will not move and they can have a great messy time.

A bowl or bucket of water nearby (safely kept) is the best way to clean up your mucky baby!

* Open and shut

Babies love looking in cupboards and opening lids or drawers and if we say 'no' they will soon do it even more to get a reaction.

I like to have a cupboard or drawer (or several) in the kitchen that they are safe to open and shut; the pot cupboard or the plastics drawer are good options. They love to copy what you are doing and at the same time are discovering how things work . . . open and shut, on and off, and so on.

Either use safety locks on cupboards or drawers you don't want your baby to play with, or just move them away gently and say 'Here is your drawer. What can we find in there?' Put 'new' things in their drawer every three days or so to keep their interest.

SAYING 'NO'

What I love about babies at this age is their increased ability to understand your words and their eagerness to be involved with whatever you are doing – if you allow them to be! The time and interest we put into our children in these early months of independent exploration are crucial and influence their future development and behaviour.

Sadly it is all too easy to become impatient with this inquisitive stage of their development and say 'No' to them, rather than using techniques to distract and divert their attention to safer or more appropriate activities. In my opinion, saying 'No' to your baby is no bad thing in itself; rather it is how often and in what way you use the word.

For babies of this age, my preferred behaviour-management tools are 'distraction and interaction'. These mean taking the baby's attention from an undesirable behaviour or activity and transferring it to something more appropriate.

When you pay attention to a baby's 'negative' behaviour, it can unintentionally reinforce it. For example, when left to play quietly while a parent is busy with jobs, a baby quickly learns that they can get the parent's attention by touching something they shouldn't, and so increasingly the baby does what you would prefer them not to do! Using distraction can prevent such a situation developing.

However, where their safety is concerned (for example, your baby is crawling towards a heater), we do need to let them know that it is not safe. In these cases I suggest you start by moving your baby away and at the same time saying confidently, but not too strongly, 'Oooh, that's hot, we don't touch that'. The idea is to physically move them away from the heater, using words of distraction along with the movement. Then, if your baby shows repeated interest in the heater, firmly say, 'No, hot. We do not touch,' and move them away from the heater with a serious expression on your face.

Learning to use distraction does take more time in the beginning and requires greater input from you, their parent. Often we can be tired from work, and have more interruptions and demands on our attention from things such as computers and smart phones than previous generations had, and so we can struggle to find the time and patience for it. However, creating gentle boundaries for your baby through your words and actions is important. If you enable time together with your baby and a positive learning environment, with consistency and repetition you will have long-reaching success.

CHAPTER 8

routines

I have discovered during my years of helping parents with their babies that whether to implement a routine or not is a common question.

Why, how and when to implement a routine

In my opinion, if we were living with extended family like we did in the past and like a lot of cultures still do around the world then, no, we might not need the sort of routine that many Westerners use today. Mothers in these communities have often grown up with small children around them and have more support from the extended family, allowing them more time to recover from the birth and help at hand to answer the daily questions associated with being a new parent.

In the modern Western world, we use the clock to run our daily life, so when it comes to our daily routines, we use time as the reminder and guide.

When I first started working on a 24-hour basis, I soon discovered a new appreciation for routine. First hand, family after family, I witnessed and experienced the challenges that parents commonly face, and the benefits of routine.

When a new baby arrives in your life, you are suddenly struck with an abundance of emotions – from immense joy to complete confusion. A lot of the confusion is caused by not being able to predict or understand your baby's cry, conflicting advice and the uncertainty this brings, especially if you have come from a career where you are in control and you provide the answers or advice. How you feel as a parent has a direct link to the happiness of your baby, so when you lack confidence because, for example, you do not know if your baby is tired or in pain, then your baby can sense this emotion.

We know that all babies are different, therefore, while a routine can be incredibly beneficial for some it may be a constraint for others. There is no right or wrong, as you have heard me say before, just do whatever works for you as a parent and what helps create an environment in which your baby can be happy and healthy.

The idea of routine can be frowned upon today, often due to the practices of the past, when it was thought that all babies should fit into the same routine. Looking into why previous generations did what they did and what errors they made got me thinking – if I took the good from the past and added in a bit of the 'new' I could create a great guide for new parents. Instead of the strict, one-style-fits-all theory, a routine should be based on your baby's health and personality and your family's needs.

Please note that the ages I have suggested for all the following routines will differ from baby to baby depending on their individual growth and development. Please seek advice, if you are uncertain whether a particular routine is suitable for your baby.

POSITIVES OF IMPLEMENTING A ROUTINE

- Helps you to understand the different cries of a baby.
- Gives you confidence.
- Gives those who have little or no support a chance to rest or cope with daily necessities.
- Lets your baby be more settled due to the consistent days and confidence in the mother.
- Helps parents to respect the baby's need to have rest and quiet time and learn how the lack of consistency and quiet time can cause some newborn babies to be unsettled.
- Gives a father or partner more opportunity to be involved.

Sleeping patterns and routines

All babies have sleeping patterns that are very similar. Below I have outlined the average awake time a baby will cope with at different points in their first year. While some parents choose to follow their baby's cues for their sleep times, I believe that some babies need help in knowing when and how to sleep.

0–3 weeks

Your baby may be sleeping most of the day and awake for around 1 hour at a time, which includes their feed and interaction time. Sometimes they might only be awake for 40 minutes and, occasionally, it may be 1 hour 10 minutes. You should put them to bed when you see their first tired sign when possible.

Your baby will be sleeping 2–3 hours between feeds but occasionally will sleep less, waking hungry. This is an important time for them to gain weight. They need to sleep to be able to feed. Wake your baby 3–4 hourly if they have not woken on their own.

4–6 weeks

Your baby should be able to cope with having a little floor play or a few outings during the week. By now their time awake is between 1¼ and 1½ hours, occasionally longer in the evening if they have slept well in the day.

Your baby will still be sleeping 2–3 hours between most feeds with some babies sleeping longer at night, up to 4–5 hours at a stretch (on a 3–4-hour routine). They will be having 3–4 daytime sleeps.

7–13 weeks

Generally your baby will be awake for 1¼–2 hours at a time now, but this will vary depending on how much you are doing in the day and how much activity your baby can cope with. The awake time at the beginning of the day is usually the smallest and increases in length as the day goes on (provided they sleep well). A baby of this age may have several days when they can cope with staying awake for 2 hours but will then require a catch-up day once or twice a week, only managing 1¼–1½ hours awake.

Your baby will be having three day sleeps (on a 3½–4-hour routine).

4–6 months

Your baby will cope with being awake for 1¾–2½ hours at a time now (depending on the time of day). They may even last up to 3 hours for their last awake time of the day, which includes bath time, if they have slept well during the day.

Your baby will still need three day sleeps (on a 3½–4-hour routine), but the time of these will depend on your individual routine and activities.

7–9 months

Your baby's time awake will increase to 2½–3½ hours (depending on the time of day).

Your baby will still need three day sleeps (on a 4-hour routine), but the times they occur may change.

10–12 months

Your baby may be awake for 2½–4 hours (depending on the time of day).

Your baby will need only two sleeps a day for most of the week; one in the morning and one in the afternoon.

Suggested routines

Weeks 1 and 2 routine

During these first weeks as parents you need to establish several important things:

1. Bonding.
2. Correct feeding positions and good milk supply.
3. Recovery from birth.
4. Coping with visitors and sharing your new baby with family and friends.

It is not important to get straight into a routine at the beginning, but for the first week, and possibly the second, I suggest creating a guide for each day, one that starts from the first feed of the day and differs in timing.

In a notebook, write down when you feed your baby, for how long and which breast (or how much formula), as well as how long they are awake for and how long they sleep. Writing down this information will help you remember, if you need to discuss it with your midwife, and is a guide for you both as tired new parents!

* **Daily routine**
- Feed your baby every 2–3 hours. Wake them, if necessary, when they have reached 3 hours (from the beginning of the previous feed). Or feed them on demand when they wake and are hungry.
- Feed your baby on one breast or half a bottle, change their nappy and then give them the other breast or second half of the bottle.
- Your baby should be awake for a maximum of 1 hour.
- Bath your baby halfway through a feed or after a feed so they are not too tired to feed efficiently.
- After the last feed at night (9–10pm), leave your baby to sleep and wake on their own. Do not wake them unless your midwife has asked you to due to low weight gain.

Writing down this information will help you remember, if you need to discuss it with your midwife, and is a guide for you both as tired new parents!

Suggested routine: Stage 1
(roughly 0–6 weeks)

In the first 6 weeks, the foundation weeks, I advise you to limit the amount of time you take your baby out. The 'old' advice was one day out, two days at home. However, I would say that for the first 3–4 weeks one day out 3–4 days at home is better. Going out for a short walk each day is fine, it is more the times that you go to someone else's house or shopping that need to be limited. Where possible cut back on some activities or ask for help from friends or family.

It is a good idea to settle your baby somewhere other than their bed (like a buggy) at home as this will help them be more adaptable in the future. It is not crucial, but transferring a baby from a buggy to a bed in their initial weeks will enable them to cope better with it in the future. Using a settling technique to help the transfer will be helpful.

I have included an example of how to approach a day when you have an appointment or outing at the end of the Stage 1 routine (see page 152).

* How long are babies on the Stage 1 routine?

A lot of babies at around 4 weeks of age might show you signs that they do not want to be woken and fed 3–3½ hourly and these signs are:
• You have to wake to feed them for every feed.
• When you wake them they don't feed as well as before, fussing slightly.

When you notice these two things occurring, try my Stage 2 routine, which is a 3½–4-hourly routine. Your baby will let you know whether they are ready for it by then either waking of their own accord 3½–4 hours after their last feed, or when you wake them they will be hungry, feeding well again.

Stage 1 Daily Routine

• First Feed: 6–6.30am

Feed and put baby straight back to bed when they have finished. This should take no longer than 1 hour. This is a good time to express if you are looking at increasing or keeping a good supply or for those who would like to stock the fridge or freezer. Have some breakfast and creep back into bed if you get the chance!

• Second Feed: 9–9.30am

If your baby was hard to settle after the last feed you can leave them an extra half an hour to help them have enough sleep to feed well. For example, if they fed at 6am but did not settle until 7.30am, instead of waking them at

9am (three hours from last feed) I would leave them until 9.30am. How long they stay up after this feed will depend upon when they woke up. (Total time awake is 1–1¼ hours maximum.) Read the signs they give you: if you try to get them to play, but they are grizzly and they have been up just over an hour, then they will be tired and you should settle them.

Once your baby is settled have a snack and glass of water to help your energy level and milk supply for the rest of the day!

• **Third Feed: 12–12.30pm**

You may find that if your baby slept and settled well at their last two feed/sleep cycles they might be able to cope with being awake for slightly longer than before, but this is not the case with all babies. You can trial this by increasing their time awake by 5–10 minutes and if they still settle well that is a sign the increased time was okay.

If you did not get a chance to have a snack during the morning, I would suggest you grab a quick bite to eat before your baby feeds as by the time you finish the feed and settle your baby you will be getting quite tired and might be tempted to skip lunch.

• **Fourth Feed: 3–3.30pm**

Time spent awake is the same as above. They may cope a little longer than the usual 1–1¼ hours at this time of day. If they wake early from their sleep after this feed, go for a walk or have snuggles to help them last until the 5.30–6pm feed.

Your afternoon snack will be your booster. A lot of mums crave sugar at this time of day, but try a miso soup or savoury muffin instead as the energy you will get from these will be longer lasting. A small snack with sugar is not a no-no, but just have a small amount!

• **Fifth Feed: 5.30–6pm**

This is the time of day when a lot of mums experience difficulty with their babies. While bath time does not need to happen every night, I like to 'split' feed at this time of day. If your baby is not awake by 6pm, wake them and feed one breast or ½–¾ of their bottle. If your baby is not happy with just having one breast before their bath or wash, feed both sides now. Generally, it is the hungry babies or mothers with a lower supply of milk who I would suggest this to. This helps with settling later in the evening. Your baby will have a good feed before a bath or wash and not be too frantic in the bath or after the bath due to hunger.

• **Bath time**

I run the bath before their 5.30–6pm feed so that it is ready to go and you do not take too long to get your baby bathed, fed and back to bed. Their awake time over this feed, bath, feed routine can be slightly longer than during the day; however, you do need to be conscious that they are not up for too long, roughly 1¼–1½ hours at most.

A baby should always love their bath so, if you are experiencing an unsettled baby at this time, it will relate to hunger, wind, bath water temperature or them being tired after a 'big day'. If you are bathing them every other day, I would 'top and tail' them, washing their face and bottom, at this time and place them in their sleeping outfit.

• Sixth Feed: 6.30–7pm

This part of the feed should be nice, quiet and calming; however, unless there is too much going on in the lounge you do not need to go into a different room, just move and talk in a quieter and slower manner.

If you are finding that your baby will not settle easily at this time of night, you need to think about how long they were awake for prior to bedtime. If they had a busy day with outings or visitors it may be they are very stimulated and their awake time should not be for too long; they may also need more snuggle and calming time before being put into bed. If they have slept well during the day and there has been limited stimulation, your baby may like to be awake for a little longer than normal, 1¼–1½ hours instead of the usual 1–1¼ hours.

It is good to flexible in these early weeks. If they are not settled to sleep within 20–30 minutes and are looking to suck, I would offer them a 5–10-minute top-up, swaddle, wind and then settle them back into bed.

• Seventh Feed (Dream Feed): 9.30–10.30pm (optional)

The idea of the dream feed is to teach your baby to sleep for the longest possible time post this feed and not post the 6.30pm feed. It really is there to help you, too, as the mother, because if you feed now hopefully your baby will sleep until 2–3am and you will not be woken at 1am, 4am and then 6.30am. It really is a personal thing, some mums do not like to do this feed and that is okay. Some babies will still manage to sleep through to 2–3am, particularly the bigger babies.

• Middle of the night feed

Now, depending on how well your baby is gaining weight (your midwife or doctor should be happy with their growth), you can choose whether you wake your baby in the night or let them wake on their own.

When the weight gain is good I like to let the baby wake on their own, thus helping to teach them the difference between night and day. You wake and feed regularly during the day and then let them sleep longer at night. Most babies will wake sometime between 1 and 2am to start with and then start sleeping longer until 2–3am and so on.

* **Juggling the different waking times in the morning**

If while your baby is on this routine they start waking later than 4am it helps to know how to juggle the morning/day waking and feeding times. If they wake at 4am you would wake and feed them again at:

- 7–7.30am
- 10–10.30am
- 1–1.30pm
- 4–4.30pm
- 6.30–7pm
- 10.30–11pm

If they wake at 5am you would wake and feed them again at:

- 8.30–9am
- 11.30–12pm
- 2.30–3pm
- 5.30–6pm
- 9.30–10.30pm

* **Appointments and outings**

It is handy to know how to juggle your routine when you have an appointment or outing. Below is an example of how to 'tweak' the daily routine to aim for a usual bedtime.

Baby woke	Feed length	Sleep	Awake	Comment
6.15am	40 minutes	7am	9.30am	Transferred to buggy at 8.45am and walked to appointment. Woke at 9.30am.
9.30am	20 minutes	10am	11.30am	Woke when transferred to bed at home so topped up with milk for 10 minutes, back to bed.
1pm	30 minutes	2.15pm	4pm	Due to outing, let her sleep until 1pm.
4pm	35 minutes	4.45pm	6.30pm	Woke, bathed before feeding due to short sleep and then fed.
6.50pm	30 minutes	7.30pm	10.30pm	I went to bed at 8.30 and woke her at 10.30pm.

Suggested routine: Stage 2
(roughly 4–6 weeks to 4–5 months)

Your baby is now starting to be more responsive and their ability to cope with more stimulation has increased slightly but you still need to allow them to sleep often so they can feed well throughout the day and be settled in the evening or during the night when you are more tired and need rest.

The Stage 2 routine is what I call a mixed routine; not a strict 4-hour routine unless your baby is a 'textbook' baby, but a mix of both a 3- and 4-hour routine, depending on the time of day.

I find that babies are at their sleepiest in the morning but are also more than likely to be hungry because they have slept for a longer period at night.

During the first 6–8 weeks your baby will go through a growth spurt and so I have created a 'When your day runs early' alternative (see page 157). This variance on routine for this age is very helpful for mums with preschool or school-aged children as pick-up and drop off times often interfere with a newborn baby's sleeping times.

The changes you will see during their time on this routine:
Several little changes will occur during this stage, because your baby is on this routine for quite some time. These changes are increased awake times and possibly decreased feeding times (due to being more efficient feeders). Babies develop and change constantly and just when you think you have your baby sleeping well, everything changes again!

I see a lot of babies at around 9 weeks of age who have started sleeping for short sleep cycles, which affects their ability to feed well due to decreased time between feeds and tiredness. At this stage they also become more interested in their environment and more inquisitive. It is often due to these changes that 'fussy' feeding starts.

What I make parents aware of is the fact that their baby not only has a growth spurt around now and is more hungry, but is also experiencing developmental changes and their time awake may need to increase slightly so they are tired enough to sleep through a sleep cycle.

So if your baby starts sleeping for a short sleep cycle, anywhere from 30–45 minutes (see 45-minute sleep cycles on page 105), and this means they are awake earlier than their next feed time, you need to think about increasing their awake time first thing in the morning and then throughout the day. Babies will show you tired signs at the 1-hour mark but this is often due to the routine you have created up until now. Increase their time awake gradually, in 5–10-minute increments, so that you don't suddenly have an over-tired and hard-to-settle baby.

Stage 2 Daily Routine

● **First Feed: 6.30–7am**

Wake your baby by 7am (if they have not woken earlier) unless you have had an unsettled time in the early hours of the morning, in which case you would wake them by 7.30am. *NOTE: You are waking them at this time so their bedtime is between 6.30 and 7.30pm. If you let them sleep until 8am, they will not be ready to go into their deeper night sleep until 8–9pm.*

This first feed of the day can often be quite small because they have slept for a longer period at night and, like us, they have a smaller 'breakfast' and as the day goes on their appetite increases. At this feed your milk supply should be good as you have had more rest than at the end of the day, for example.

Feed your baby and put back to bed sometime between 1 hour 10 minutes and 1½ hours later, depending on how old they are and how well they usually sleep after this feed. If you find that they are waking earlier than 9.15–10am then you need to keep them up for a little longer after this feed. So, to begin with (4–6 weeks in age), you feed and put back to bed after an hour roughly, but by the time they are 9 weeks this time will increase (1 hour 20 minutes to 1½ hours) and they will have quiet play (in your arms or in a bouncer) before bed.

● **Second Feed: 9.30–10am**

Just like with the Stage 1 routine, you can leave your baby sleeping until 10.30am, half an hour later than suggested above, if they took a while to settle prior to this sleep or if they are sound asleep and feed better for you if given that extra half hour.

Feed as close to waking as possible (unless they wake earlier than hoped) as I find they feed better when they are sleepy and before they are distracted by what is going on around them. After they have fed I give them digestion time, meaning time sitting in a baby chair or on the floor propped up on a feeding pillow (or sitting with you talking!) for say 5–10 minutes and then try for a burp before lying them flat on the floor under a baby gym. This is a good time to have nappy-free time.

Their time awake may be able to be a little longer (increase by just 10 minutes or so) than their last if they had a good sleep.

This is a good time to have a little outing. Coffee groups, antenatal groups and community activities are often at this time of day. It may be necessary for you to 'tweak' the timings of your routine so you can get out in time. Just be wary not to overdo these morning activities, as their sleep in the morning will determine the rest of the day's flow. Majority/minority rule! I like to try to get back in time for their sleep at home. If your baby falls asleep in the car just before you get home, try transferring them, or offer your baby a 'top-up' on the breast or a small bottle and put them to bed about 20–30 minutes later. A short nap in the car for older babies (12 weeks plus) will often make them feel like they have had their sleep and if you attempt to put them straight to bed they will protest.

- **Third Feed: 1.30–2pm**

Follow the advice above with a possible increase in their time awake if they slept well or even a decrease in their time awake if they were unsettled or you had an outing.

If you have been out in the morning I would try to stay home for this sleep as this will help their evening settling time; however, if you struggle to get your baby to sleep well in the afternoon, I would think about either taking them for a walk for the 'rest' of their sleep (when waking early) or ending the day following my suggestions for 'When your day runs early' (see page 157). Your baby may need an extra little feed and sleep to make it to a 7–7.30pm bedtime.

- **Fourth Feed: 5–5.30pm**

Again, this time of day is when a lot of mums experience difficulty settling their babies after they have fed. 'Cluster' or 'split' feeding around their bath time is a good idea. (See Stage 1: Fifth Feed on page 150.) *NOTE: If you are following the 'When your day runs early' suggestion (see page 157), I suggest you bath the baby without a feed first as their last small feed was at 4pm. You will have to trial this as it is different for each baby; some feed better if you give them bigger gaps between feeds and some need to feed frequently due to a breastfeeding mother's lower milk supply at this time of day.*

- **Bath time**

I run the bath before their 5–5.30pm feed so that it is ready once they have fed. Their awake time over this feed, bath, feed routine can be slightly longer than during the day; by 3–4 months they may last up to 2 hours over this time. (See also Stage 1: Bath time on page 150.)

During this stage of development I might think about bathing or showering with your baby; they should feel comfortable being naked and handled.

- **Fifth Feed: 6.30–7pm**

This feed, like with the previous routine, should be in a quieter environment. By now your baby will be able to sit with you for a short story or you can read to your baby while you are feeding them.

I would suggest that you do not take too long putting your baby to bed if you are struggling to settle them at this time of night. If they are unsettled, look at how long you have kept them awake for (maybe you are trying to put them down too early or you have kept them up too long). Some babies simply love the quiet snuggle time as you wind them down in their room before sleep and don't like you putting them down, especially when they are not tired enough! It is best to have quality reading time out of the room and then have a cuddle, swaddle and put into bed in a shorter time. Being in their room for some of their activity time, not just sleep-associated time, can help them enjoy their room more!

This bedtime might need to be more like 7–7.30pm if your baby had a later sleep, waking at 5.30pm, and they are 9 weeks or more.

• **Sixth Feed (Dream Feed): 10–11pm (optional)**
As with the Stage 1 routine, the dream feed is optional. It does not suit all mums, but it will extend the time your baby sleeps until 2–3am, meaning you may not have to get up as many times to feed in the night.

The time of this feed is dependent on how well your baby settles after the fifth feed and how long you choose to stay awake for. If you go to bed before the dream feed then I would make it 11pm but if you are more of a night owl then I would do it sometime between 10 and 10.30pm.

Some parents will choose to offer a breastfed baby a bottle of milk that was expressed earlier in the day (usually slightly fattier) or milk that was expressed before waking the baby for this feed. I often suggest this as an idea if I see a mother struggling with tiredness as the father can feed the baby the bottle and she can have an extra 2–3 hours sleep if going to bed after dinner. It is important to express before you go to bed if you struggle with an over-supply at the middle of the night feed or if you want to keep up a good supply of milk.

NOTE: *Most babies do not need to be winded as much at this time of night because they are tired and feeding slowly – dream feeding.*

• **Middle of the night feed**
This will probably be anywhere from 2–3am when they start on this routine and gradually will become later and later until they are possibly sleeping through until morning.

If you are struggling with settling your baby after this feed and you think they are suffering from digestion trouble I would think about what you had for dinner or the possibility of feeding lying down if your milk supply is very active. Babies often do not need as much winding at night if the feed is calm and sleepy.

* Juggling the different waking times in the morning

If your baby wakes after 4–4.30am give them a smaller feed, put them back to bed and then 'finish off' by offering the other breast at 6.30–7am. If they wake closer to 5–5.30am do the same, but I would leave them until 7.30am if they are still sound asleep at 7am. A lot of babies will struggle to feed at their first feed of the day (6.30–7am) if they have had a large feed at these earlier times. If this is the case, feeding your baby just one breast side or a smaller bottle so it is almost like a 'split' feed is advisable. You will know if it is suitable for you and your baby if they settle well. (I would keep them swaddled and the feed would be a quick feed, no nappy change unless it is dirty.)

If your baby wakes a little later (at 7.30am) then you might 'tweak' your routine as follows:

- First feed: 7.30am
- Second feed: 10.30–11am
- Third feed: 2–2.30pm
- Continue as per usual afternoon/evening timing above

* When your day runs early

Sometimes your day runs early, normally because your baby has had a shorter sleep than usual or you have had to go out. When this happens I add in an extra half-hour sleep at the end of the day between 4.30 and 5pm, waking them at the latest at 5.30pm.

So your day might look like this:

- 9.30am: Feed
- 10.45–11am: Sleep time. Woke early at 1pm. Would not settle, was hungry and so . . .
- 1pm: Feed
- 2.30pm: Sleep time. Woke at 4pm
- 4pm: Small feed
- 4.45–5pm: Small extra sleep. Wake at 5.30pm
- Continue as per usual evening timing above

Suggested routine: Stage 3

(roughly 4–5 months to 7 months)

I like to think of this routine as your baby's transition routine or phase as they are heading towards only requiring two sleeps a day. We reduce the length of the day sleeps during this stage, which means you can increase their night sleeping times or keep up a 7–7.30pm bedtime. They are being introduced to solid food somewhere during these 2–3 months, which also aids their night-time sleeping.

You know your baby is ready for this routine when you struggle to get them to sleep for long periods at their morning or afternoon sleeps.

In this case, I like to keep their morning sleep as a good quality sleep rather than a short 45-minute sleep (majority/minority rule) as I know they will then cope better with the day and also when they move to two sleeps a day they will need a good morning sleep to be able to cope.

Their time awake can increase again and you will be guided by how well they settle and how long they sleep for. So, for example, if your baby is waking at 6.30am at 5 months of age they should be able to stay awake for 2–2½ hours (depending on how often they wake in the night). Again, you may have to spend 3–5 days slowly pushing out the time they are awake by 5–10 minutes, if they are currently only awake for 1½–2 hours.

Some parents prefer their babies to have a short sleep in the morning as it means they can get out more often but, with most babies I see, it can affect the rest of the day and their ability to cope with their increasing physical skills and to try new things, like solids and outside activities.

As your baby approaches 7 months you may find that they will transition to the Stage 4 routine by having two sleeps a day 1–2 days a week and then going back to the Stage 3 routine for the rest of the week, depending on what happens during the morning and afternoon. You know when your baby is ready to move on to two sleeps a day when you can no longer get them to go down for their lunchtime sleep or late afternoon nap, or you struggle to get them down to sleep at 7–7.30pm.

Stage 3 Daily Routine

- **First Feed: 6.30–7am**

Feed your baby on waking and then give them some playtime. Place your baby in a baby chair or sit them supported by pillows where they can see what is going on. At this stage your baby likes to watch what you are doing, like eating your breakfast or helping other children in the family to get dressed.

- **Breakfast: 7–7.30am**

This would be the second or third meal that I would introduce (see Introducing solid food on page 124) and I would offer it about ½–1 hour after their milk feed. After some watching time (digestion time when they were smaller), I would give them some floor play, or this would be a great time to go for a walk, especially in the hotter months when, in some areas, it can become too hot after 9am.

Sleep time is around 8.30–9am and this sleep will be anywhere from 1–2 hours, depending on how old they are and how well they slept in the night.

- **Second Feed: 10–10.30am**

Feed your baby on waking and then this is a good time for going out or doing an activity with your baby. If you have a weekly group activity or coffee group and you need to wake your baby before this time, that is okay if you are only doing it once or twice a week (majority/minority rule). They will cope with a shorter sleep prior to this feed time as they can have a longer midday or afternoon sleep.

- **Lunch: 11–11.30am**

This would be the first meal that I would introduce and I would offer it about ½–1 hour after their milk feed.

Sleep time is between 11.30am and 12.30pm – earlier when first starting on this routine or if their morning sleep was shorter – and it would be for roughly 1½–2 hours. If your baby has a 2-hour sleep in the morning when starting on this routine, by 5½ months they might be sleeping for just 1 hour here, with their third feed being slightly earlier, like the Stage 2 routine.

- **Third Feed: 2–2.30pm**

Feed your baby on waking and then, like earlier, you can have an outing or activity time.

Sleep time is anywhere from 4–4.30pm and for only ½–1 hour, waking by 5pm at the latest. (If they had a short midday sleep, you can put them to bed by 3.30pm.)

- **Fourth Feed: 5pm**

This is just a small feed, maybe one breast or a small bottle. When your baby is closer to 7 months of age you can offer them a solid meal at this time, dropping this small milk feed. I would do this if your baby is still not interested in solid food by 7 months of age.

- **Dinner: 5–5.30pm**

This would be the second meal of the day that I would introduce. To begin with it will be at 5.30pm, after your baby has had time to digest their milk a little. By 7 months dinner should be around 5pm, as they will not be having a breastfeed on waking at 5pm.

- **Bath time**

After dinner has been digested, roughly at 5.30–6pm, I would give them a wash of some sort. I like to bath or shower the baby, if possible, as they now are enjoying this as an activity and it calms them at the same time. But a 'top and tail' wash has its place.

If you do not have a bath, you can put a plastic tub in the shower to bath them once they are sitting (just be sure to tip the water out when finished).

- **Fifth Feed: 6–6.30pm**

Feed your baby after their bath or wash, then read some stories. Have calming snuggles before putting to bed.

Sleep time is roughly 7–7.30pm, depending on how long your baby can stay awake over this time. Most babies who are waking at 5pm will be happy with a 7pm bedtime but others might need another half hour, especially those babies who are struggling to sleep more than 45 minutes at this time of night.

- **Sixth Feed (Dream Feed): 10.30–11pm**

Some babies may still need a dream feed until they are having 2–3 solid meals a day. However, this feed can become a negative if your baby is waking frequently in the night. Many parents mistake the frequent waking as hunger but it can be that by having a dream feed you are encouraging them to wake and feed frequently and they are less receptive to being woken now. So, if you are doing a dream feed but your baby is waking before 4–5am, I would think about stopping this feed, resettling instead of feeding if they wake. It may take 3–5 days to change this pattern.

- **Middle of the night feed**

By now your baby has the ability to sleep through the night if their daytime routine is good, but some will not be able to do this until they are on solid food, particularly if they are hungry and active babies. A good routine includes good milk feeds, possibly solid food, the right amount of sleep for them personally and enough physical and mental stimulation. Some babies I work with will wake even with these things in place and so that is when I ask their parents what they would like to do. Some are happy with waking just once in the night and some would like to teach their babies to sleep longer and think they are waking due to habits created when they were ill, teething or travelling. If this is the case, I suggest you put aside 3–5 days and try to resettle your baby (see page 118).

Suggested routine: Stage 4

(roughly 7–16 months)

A baby of 7 months and onwards is a lot more flexible with their daytime routine and can now cope if you are a little late in getting them to bed or if they nap in the car, in which case they may need a longer afternoon sleep – it is just a trial and error process!

The big difference with this routine is the introduction of feeding your baby before their morning and mid-afternoon sleeps. Until now you have been trying to feed your baby on waking, but at this stage I change that pattern as I find your baby will sleep better now because they are more active and the feed acts like a morning tea.

During this time a lot of babies will be teething and there may be times when those who used to be good sleepers, both during the day and at night, will struggle due to discomfort. You may have to be more flexible with your routine times during this period. You may also find that a 7–9-month-old baby will need less activity time and more snuggle time while they're teething.

Towards the end of your baby's time on this routine you may find that they will transition to the next stage by having one sleep a day 1–2 days a week and then going back to this Stage 4 routine for the rest of the week, depending on what happens in the morning and what activities you do daily. Your baby may be as young as 12–14 months when they show signs of dropping down to one sleep a day – these are often the active babies!

Stage 4 Daily Routine

- **First Feed: 6.30–7am**

If your baby is still asleep at this time you are fine now to leave them to wake on their own. It will just mean that they will have a shorter morning or afternoon sleep. If you keep your baby up later at night they may need to catch up in the morning.

Feed your baby on waking and then have some snuggle time or free play until breakfast.

- **Breakfast: 7–7.30am**

Your baby should not need too much digestion time by now as they are stronger physically, and so they can head straight into playtime after breakfast or you may go out for a morning walk or play at the park.

When you are starting on this routine watch that you are not out too long as you may find your baby will fall asleep in the car or buggy and then may only have a short morning sleep.

• **Second Feed: 9.30–10am**

Offer their milk feed before their first morning sleep, otherwise I find they will not sleep as long here, and at 7–8 months of age it is like their 'morning tea'.

When your baby first begins on this routine they will probably show you tired signs around 9am and therefore may not be interested in a breastfeed before the morning sleep, so you may need to use some distraction to help them last until their 'new' sleep time or feed them after their sleep (like on the Stage 3 routine) for a short time as they adapt to the new routine. Having some nappy-free time or a walk in the garden is a good way of taking their mind off what they are used to. However, you do not want to push them too far; you don't want an unhappy baby and it may be that you start with a 9–9.15am bedtime and then gradually move them to 9.30–10am after a few weeks, increasing the time you keep them up depending on how long they sleep for.

Sleep time is straight after this feed and your aim is for your baby to have a minimum of 1¼ hours' sleep and a maximum of 2 hours.

• **Lunch: 11.30am–12.30pm**

This will depend on whether they have their milk feed before or after their sleep and, of course, how long they sleep for. One reason I offer milk before their sleep is to encourage them to eat their solid food now.

After lunch enjoy playtime or an outing, depending on how much your baby likes to be stimulated.

• **Third Feed: 1.30–2pm**

Put your baby down for their afternoon sleep straight after this milk feed.

Sleep time is for 1–2 hours here, all depending on how long they slept in the morning. If their morning sleep was close to 2 hours then they may have just 1 hour in the afternoon. If your baby is struggling to settle later in the evening (7–7.30pm) or is not sleeping well at night and all their dietary needs are being met, you may need to limit this sleep time, waking your baby after 1–1½ hours rather than letting them sleep for 2 hours.

If they wake before 4pm, I would offer a small afternoon tea, maybe some fruit in a muslin or teething cloth or maybe even a breastfeed if they are not so good on solids yet.

• **Dinner: 5–5.30pm**

On days when your baby has less sleep than usual, offering dinner a little earlier is wise, say, 4–5pm instead. This will help to prevent 'fussy' feeding or unsettled behaviour.

- **Bath time**

After dinner has digested, roughly at 5.30–6pm, I would give them a bath, shower or wash.

- **Fourth Feed: 6.30–7pm**

Feed your baby after their bath or wash and then read some stories, have calming snuggles and then bedtime.

Sleep time is roughly 7–7.30pm, depending on how long your baby can stay awake over this time. Most babies who are waking at 4pm will be happy with a 7pm bedtime but others might need another half hour, especially those babies who are struggling to sleep more than 45 minutes at this time of night.

- **Middle of the night feed**

By now your baby has the ability to sleep through the night if their daytime routine is good. They may be in the habit of waking, however, if they have been ill, teething or travelling (see Night waking on page 119). If you want to encourage them to sleep through the night, I suggest you put aside 3–5 days and try to resettle your baby.

afterword

Over the past 12 years working and specialising in the baby phase of a child's development, I've come to recognise that all parents seek the same goals: to be the best parent they can be and to have a happy, healthy child who knows they are loved.

My decision to create a new parents' guide based on my professional experiences was brought about by my desire to help families all over New Zealand in all circumstances – not just those who can afford to have a postnatal carer in their homes, or who live in close enough proximity to attend my seminars and workshops.

The responses I've received from the many families I've worked with have also encouraged me to put my work experience and tried-and-tested methods into book form. Without the sure knowledge of these happy babies and parents I would not have found quite the same confidence and continuing passion to share my knowledge.

There are many books out there that can confuse parents. Confidence is what we all need to develop and instil in our children for their future, and our confidence as parents comes from how we are supported, loved and nurtured when our babies arrive into the world.

I hope and trust that *Baby Whispering* has given you the information you require and the assurance to find your own way and style of parenting, and that it has also inspired you to create a calm, loving environment in which to welcome your child, right from the beginning.

'Learning to be the best parent I can be is one of the greatest challenges I've ever faced. Having a coach to support me is one of the most intelligent things I've done.' – Sally Herbert

RECOMMENDED SERVICES AND CONTACTS

There are so many wonderful services and websites at our disposal today. I have listed a few of my favourites below. For updated contacts please visit my website www.littlemiracles.co.nz

• Specialist baby advisors and in-house support

Sharlene Poole – NZ Baby Whisperer
Little Miracles Postnatal Care Ltd
www.littlemiracles.co.nz
www.babywhispering.com

Karitane Nannies and Nurses
www.karitanenannies.co.nz
(0800) 222 121 or (09) 575 7174

• Parenting Courses and Support

The Parenting Place
300 Great South Road
Greenlane, Auckland
(09) 524 0025 or (0800) 53 56 59
www.theparentingplace.co.nz

Multiple Birth Club Society
Check the website for groups
in your area.
www.multiples.org.nz

Parents Centre
Check the website to find the nearest group coordinator in your area.
www.parentscentre.org.nz

• New Zealand Health Professionals

NZ Plunket Society
Check the website to find the nearest Plunket centre in your area.
www.plunket.org.nz

PlunketLine
A 24-hour service which provides advice on parenting, nutrition, child development and behaviour for children from birth to five years.
(0800) 933 922

Quintessence
Natural Health, Mother and Baby Specialists
www.qhealth.co.nz
(09) 817 1530 or 0800 7432 584

NZ Osteopath Society
Check the website for a recommended baby specialist in your area.
www.osnz.org

Lactation Consultants
Check the website for a recommended baby specialist in your area or talk with your midwife or doctor.
www.nzlca.org.nz

Postnatal Distress Organisation
Provides free support for those affected by any or all of the symptoms and in all degrees – whether baby blues or antenatal or postnatal distress (PND).
www.postnataldistress.org.nz

Bowen Technique
A gentle form of body work that is considered appropriate for anyone from pregnant women to newborn babies.
www.bowtech.org.nz

glossary

baby-led weaning When a baby is offered finger food rather than pureed food and, by doing so, they choose how much they consume.

cluster feeding When a baby feeds frequently at the end of the day, maybe 2–3 times in the space of 2–3 hours.

'colic' A term describing a period of time in the day, often the evening, when a baby in their first 3 months of age is unsettled or cries for long periods of time.

controlled crying When you leave a baby to cry for a set amount of time before responding to help them settle.

digestion time Resting babies in an upright position after feeding to allow their milk to digest, before moving them around or lying them down flat.

foremilk The first milk that comes with a let-down, the 'thirst quencher'. This is not as creamy as the second milk, the hindmilk (see below).

hindmilk The milk that follows the foremilk, hindmilk is fattier, more satisfying and helps your baby to make good weight gain.

let-down The action that releases the milk from the milk ducts when your baby sucks, and often also happens when they cry!

reflux Gastro-oesophageal reflux disease is when babies spill their milk with feeds and cry in discomfort, which can then lead to low weight gain and refusal to feed. A variation of this is 'silent' reflux, when babies do not spill but otherwise suffer from the same symptoms as babies who do spill. Their breath can often smell sour.

rooting reflex A reflex that newborn babies are born with, so that when you touch the area either side of their mouth it tells them to turn to search for their food.

split feeding When you feed a baby half of their milk feed, bath or change them and then give them the other half of their feed after a small break.

tongue-tie Some babies are born with a tongue-tie, which is when the piece of tissue joining the tongue to the bottom of their mouth (the lingual frenum) is too short and restrictive, making it hard for baby to latch to the breast. In some cases the skin may need to be 'clipped' by a doctor to enable the baby to breastfeed well.

tummy time Turning a baby onto their tummy with their arms placed up by their head so they can try to push up with their hands and arms, lifting their head off the ground. This is to strengthen their neck and back muscles.

weaning Changing a baby's feeding habits from either breast to bottle or breast to cup.

index